D1267185

THE
RING
AND
THE
FIRE

THE RING AND THE FIRE

Stories from Wagner's Nibelung Operas

By CLYDE ROBERT BULLA

Woodcuts by Clare and John Ross

Thomas Y. Crowell Company
New York

BOOKS BY CLYDE ROBERT BULLA

The Donkey Cart
Riding the Pony Express
The Secret Valley
Surprise for a Cowboy
A Ranch for Danny
Song of St. Francis
Johnny Hong of Chinatown
Eagle Feather
Star of Wild Horse Canyon
Down the Mississippi
Squanto, Friend of the White Men
White Sails to China
The Poppy Seeds
John Billington, Friend of Squanto
The Sword in the Tree
Old Charlie
Ghost Town Treasure
Pirate's Promise
The Valentine Cat
Stories of Favorite Operas
Three-Dollar Mule
A Tree Is a Plant
The Sugar Pear Tree
Benito
The Ring and the Fire

To Lauritz Melchior,
a great Siegfried

CONTENTS

RICHARD WAGNER

RICHARD WAGNER was born in Leipzig, Germany, on May 22, 1813. His father, a clerk in a Leipzig police court, died the following November, leaving the widow with seven children. In the summer of 1814 she married Ludwig Geyer, a family friend, and she and the children moved with him to Dresden.

Geyer was a portrait painter, playwright, actor, and musician. He sang at the Dresden opera house. Richard was taken to opera performances when he was still very young, and music was a part of his home life, but at first he showed little musical talent. He was more interested in literature. By the time he was eleven, he was writing poetry and reading the works of Shakespeare.

After Geyer's death in 1821, the family stayed on in Dresden for several years, then went back to Leipzig. Richard began to study composition so that he could write music to his poems. This, in turn, led him to realize how music could add strength and meaning to his words.

1

He entered the University of Leipzig for courses in literature and fine arts. He composed a symphony and some shorter works, but his main interest was opera. As a composer, he was largely self-taught. His formal training lasted only about six months.

In 1833, when he was twenty, he became conductor and chorus master for a small opera company in Würzburg. In the next few years he held similar posts in Magdeburg, Königsberg, and Riga. The work was hard and poorly paid, but it gave him valuable theatrical experience. In the crowded years between 1833 and 1836 he managed to write two operas. The first, *The Fairies,* was never produced during his lifetime. The second, *The Ban upon Love,* had only one performance.

In Königsberg he met a young actress, Minna Planer, and married her on March 24, 1836.

In Riga he wrote the libretto and part of the music for his third opera, *Rienzi.* (Wagner wrote both the librettos and music for all his operas.) Production facilities were limited in the small German opera houses, and he had conceived the work on a grand scale. He decided to take it to Paris.

He and his wife left for France in the autumn of 1839. They sailed by way of England. The ship ran into one storm after another, and the long, wild voyage furnished Wagner with inspiration for what was to be his next opera, *The Flying Dutchman,* the story of a sea captain doomed to sail the seas forever.

Wagner and his wife lived in Paris for two and a half years. He earned a meager living by arranging and proofreading for a music publisher and by writing articles on music for various publications, but he could find no one in Paris to produce his operas.

He had finished *Rienzi* and *The Flying Dutchman*. In the summer of 1841 word came that *Rienzi* was to be produced in Dresden.

He and his wife returned to Germany to be in Dresden for the first performance of the opera. *Rienzi* was so successful that the company produced *The Flying Dutchman* a few months later.

The usual opera of the day was an entertainment made up of arias, ensemble numbers, dances, and often a procession or some other colorful spectacle. The music was far more important than the drama. In *The Flying Dutchman* Wagner had begun to break away from this form. He had come to believe that the drama should be of first importance, with the music growing out of it. The new opera was a step toward the "music drama" which he perfected in his later works and which changed the course of opera composition.

Audiences were not yet ready to accept *The Flying Dutchman*. They found it strange and gloomy.

Wagner's opera *Tannhäuser,* produced in 1845, had only a fair success. In 1848 he finished the opera *Lohengrin,* and could find no one to produce it.

He had made many enemies, partly because of his musical ideas, partly because of his political views. In 1848-49 there were uprisings against the German government, and Wagner sided with the revolutionists. A warrant was issued for his arrest. His friend Franz Liszt, the pianist-composer, helped him escape to Switzerland.

For the next ten years Wagner was an exile. Most of this time he lived in Switzerland. He had become interested in tales of the legendary hero Siegfried, and in 1848 he had finished a libretto called *Siegfried's Death.*

Afterward it seemed to him that the poem contained too much material for a single opera. During his exile he wrote a poem, *Young Siegfried,* telling of the hero's early life.

Feeling that *Young Siegfried* needed further explanation, he wrote a poem *The Valkyrie,* which told of events leading up to the hero's birth. This called for still another poem, *The Rhinegold,* which told of happenings before the beginning of *The Valkyrie.*

These were the librettos, written in reverse order, for the opera cycle called *The Ring of the Nibelung.* Wagner changed the title *Siegfried's Death* to *The Dusk of the Gods. Young Siegfried* became *Siegfried.*

Wagner based his *Ring of the Nibelung* on tales of Norse and German mythology. Some of the stories appeared more than a thousand years ago in the *Edda,* a collection of Norse legends. Others were collected in the *Nibelungenlied,* an epic poem of the twelfth century.

In the legends, as in Greek mythology, gods mingled with mortals and took part in affairs of the earth. Mightiest of the gods was Wotan, also known as Odin or Woden. He roamed the earth in various disguises, and sometimes he appeared as an old one-eyed man wearing a robe and a wide-brimmed hat. Ravens and wolves were associated with him.

4

Fricka, Wotan's wife, was the goddess of married love.

Freia, her sister, was the goddess of youth and beauty.

Loge, or Loki, the fire god, was pictured as handsome and cunning.

Donner was the impetuous god of thunder.

Erda, the earth goddess, was guardian of wisdom.

The Valkyries ("Choosers of the Slain") were daughters of Wotan and Erda. These half-savage warrior maidens hovered over battlefields, gathered up the bodies of slain heroes, and carried them off to Valhalla.

Valhalla ("Hall of the Slain") was the fortress and dwelling place of the gods.

Giants and water nymphs lived on earth.

Gnomes lived in an underground realm.

Among these gods, half-gods, and earthly beings moved the hero Siegfried.

Wagner planned *The Ring* as a cycle of three operas and a prelude, to be given on four successive evenings. The prelude, as he called *The Rhinegold,* was meant to be performed without pause, although in today's productions it is sometimes divided into four separate scenes.

Between 1853 and 1856 he composed *The Rhinegold, The Valkyrie,* and part of *Siegfried.* Then, in the second act of *Siegfried,* he gave up in despair. No opera company was equipped to perform such a monumental work. He had little hope that it could ever be produced.

He turned to another opera, *Tristan and Isolde,* and finished the score in 1859, although it was not performed until six years later. In 1861 Wagner went to Paris to conduct *Tannhäuser.* He would not bow to public demand and add a ballet to his opera, and the production was a disaster.

It was during this time of disappointment and discouragement that he wrote the libretto of his only comic opera, *The Mastersingers of Nuremberg*. The opera was finished in 1867. Its first performance was in Munich the following year.

By this time he was no longer an exile. In 1864 King Ludwig of Bavaria had called him to Munich. The eighteen-year-old monarch was an ardent admirer of Wagner's music, which had been widely performed in Germany during the composer's banishment.

Wagner and the king planned to transform Munich into a world music center. A magnificent theater was designed, and it was to be linked to the royal palace by a new avenue and a bridge.

But Wagner had powerful enemies in Munich. Politicians attacked his extravagance and his political views. In 1865 so much pressure was brought to bear on King Ludwig that he asked his friend to leave Munich.

Wagner went back to Switzerland and lived for a while near Lucerne. He was still in the royal favor, and the king insisted on having *The Rhinegold* and *The Valkyrie* given in Munich. This was against Wagner's wishes. He had not wanted any of the *Ring* operas given until they could be produced in a theater specially built for the cycle. King Ludwig was ready to have the theater built in Munich, but the composer's enemies kept the plan from being carried out.

Wagner's wife, Minna, died in 1866. Four years later

he married Cosima, daughter of his friend Franz Liszt.

Meanwhile, he had gone back to *The Ring,* and the cycle was finished in 1872. The special theater was built at last—not in Munich, but in the town of Bayreuth. The complete *Ring of the Nibelung* was given there in the summer of 1876.

In 1879 he finished *Parsifal,* his last opera. Its first performance was in the Bayreuth theater in 1882.

Wagner's health had begun to fail. He became suddenly ill during a visit to Venice, and he died there on February 13, 1883.

THE RHINEGOLD

SCENE 1

IN THE DAYS when gods and lesser supernatural beings inhabited the earth, three water nymphs lived a carefree life in the River Rhine. Their father had charged them to guard a mysterious treasure that lay on a peak at the bottom of the stream, and they watched over it faithfully, although they had little fear that it would ever be stolen from them.

9

The treasure was the Rhinegold. It was small in size, but its magical powers were great. If the gold were fashioned into a ring, he who possessed it might rule the world. But only one who had renounced love forever had the power to seize the Rhinegold and shape it into a ring.

So the nymphs guarded the treasure lightheartedly, for who in all the world could live without love?

One day the nymph Woglinde swam alone about the rocky peak on which the Rhinegold had been placed for safekeeping. On all sides were smaller peaks rising out of the dark depths into the greenish twilight of the river.

Woglinde's sister, Wellgunde, called from above, "Do you watch alone?"

"Yes," answered Woglinde, "until you come."

Wellgunde dived down to the high rock beside her. Woglinde darted away. Playfully the two tried to catch each other.

The third maiden, Flosshilde, swam down from above and came between her sisters.

"You guard the sleeping gold badly," she reproved them, but almost at once she joined in the game. Laughing and shouting, the three went swimming back and forth like fish.

A gnome crept out of a chasm in the river bed. He was Alberich, a Nibelung from the underground realm of Nibelheim. He watched the Rhinemaidens in delight.

"Ho, ho, you nixies!" he called out to them.

The maidens peered down through the water and were alarmed to see the hairy, misshapen figure leering up at them.

"Look to the gold!" cried Flosshilde, and the sisters gathered protectingly about the rock where the treasure lay.

"Do I spoil your sport?" asked Alberich. "Dive deeper then. A Nibelung longs to frolic with you."

The Rhinemaidens were bewildered.

"Is this his joke?" asked Wellgunde.

Alberich continued in a languishing voice, "How soft and fair you seem! How sweet to circle a maid with my arm, if she should kindly descend!"

"Our foe is in love!" Flosshilde said to her sisters, and the stranger was no longer someone to fear, but only a ridiculous creature to be scorned and despised.

"Let us content him," said Woglinde mischievously, and she dived to a lower rock and invited the gnome to come closer.

Eagerly he climbed toward her. His hands and feet slipped on the slimy stone. The chill of the water crept up his nose, and he sneezed.

"See how nicely my sweetheart can sneeze!" said Woglinde.

"Be mine, you beautiful child!" panted the gnome, toiling to the summit of the rock.

But Woglinde swam away and alighted on another rock.

"Alas, you are lost! Come nearer!" pleaded Alberich.

She darted from rock to rock, and as he went floundering after her, she laughed and moved out of reach.

Wellgunde swam to a low rock.

"My hero!" she called to Alberich. "Come to *me!*"

The gnome decided at once that she was more beautiful than the other, and he went stumbling toward her.

But she, too, slipped away from him. "Horrible imp!" she taunted him. "Look for a sweetheart fit for your shape!"

"Chilly, slippery fish!" bellowed Alberich. "Go and let eels be your lovers!"

Flosshilde spoke. "You have sought only two. Now try the third one."

"Your song sounds sweet in my ear," the gnome said warily, "but before I believe you, come nearer."

Flosshilde dived down to him. Her sisters were senseless, she said, not to recognize his charms. Tenderly she drew him to her, calling him "dearest of men."

"Sweetest of maidens!" he said in ecstasy.

"Were you but mine!" she said. "Your staring-eyed brow and your straggle-haired beard—if only I could keep them forever!"

Woglinde and Wellgunde had drawn near, and at this tender speech of their sister's they burst out laughing.

Alberich started. "Are you laughing at me?"

"Yes," said Flosshilde. "That is the end of my song," and she pushed him away.

She and her sisters rose through the water, and Alberich screamed after them in rage. He sprang from rock to rock, trying to catch first one then another. Always they kept just beyond his reach, until at last he gave up the chase.

As he stood, speechless with exhaustion and fury, a glow of light broke through the waters. He gazed in wonder. The light grew brighter, kindling a golden radiance on the peak of the highest rock.

It was the gold, exclaimed the Rhinemaidens. The gold was smiling, waking from its sleep.

The gnome gazed in fascination. "What is it," he asked, "that glows and gleams?"

The maidens answered him, "Where is your home, you imp, if you have never heard of the Rhinegold?"

"If it shines only to light your play," said Alberich, "it would do me small good."

"You would indeed prize the gold if you knew of its wonders," Woglinde told him.

"The one who can shape the Rhinegold into a ring can have measureless power," said Wellgunde.

"This our father told us, and he bade us guard the treasure from all foes," said Flosshilde.

"But," said Woglinde, "only one who has renounced love shall be the ring's master."

"So we are safe and free from care," said Wellgunde, "for surely no one can live without loving."

"Least of all this lovesick gnome," said Woglinde, and the sisters looked scornfully down on Alberich.

He had listened carefully to the Rhinemaidens' words. A sudden, fierce resolve came to him. Love had been denied him—then he would renounce it and choose power instead.

He flung himself at the high rock and began to claw his way up.

The maidens swam away, half-delirious with excitement.

13

"Save yourselves!" they cried to one another. "The monster is mad! Love has driven him insane!"

Alberich reached the summit of the rock. "Go in darkness—I put out your light," he shouted, "and with a ring I shall have vengeance!"

In a terrible burst of strength, he tore the gold from the rock. With the treasure clutched in his hand, he plunged from the peak.

Darkness fell.

"Stop the robber! Rescue the gold!" shrieked the Rhinemaidens. "Woe! Woe!"

And as the darkness deepened, Alberich's mocking laughter sounded from the depths.

SCENE 2

On a mountaintop overlooking the valley of the Rhine, Wotan, mightiest of the gods, lay sleeping. Fricka, his wife, slept nearby. Beyond the valley rose a cliff on which stood a magnificent castle with battlements and towers that glistened in the early morning light.

Fricka wakened, saw the castle, and started in surprise. She roused her husband.

Wotan raised his head and gazed at the shining fortress. "It is finished!" he said in rapture. This was the fulfillment of his dreams—a glorious dwelling place for the gods.

Fricka did not share his joy. "It is finished, the debt is now due," she reminded him. "Have you forgotten what you must give?"

Two giants, Fafner and Fasolt, had built the castle according to Wotan's plans. In return, he had promised them the lovely Freia, who was Fricka's sister and the goddess of youth and beauty.

Wotan reminded his wife in turn, "You yourself longed for this castle."

It was true, she admitted. She had hoped that in the new dwelling place he would be content to stay at home beside her. Now she realized that he had wanted the castle as a means of making himself more powerful in the world.

"If you would keep me near you at home," said Wotan, "then I must have my own way in the world. I am a god, and I cannot give up my pleasures."

Fricka became bitterly accusing. "You love me no longer. A woman's love means nothing to you."

"As you well know," answered Wotan gravely, "I wagered and lost an eye to win you for my wife." He denied that he cared nothing for a woman's love. "I worship women. I worship them too much for your happiness. I'll not let Freia be taken from us. That was not my plan."

"Then protect her now," said Fricka, "for here she comes."

Freia came in sight, crying out in terror. "Help me! Fasolt is coming to carry me away!"

Wotan asked her, "Did you not see Loge?"

It was Loge, crafty god of fire, who had helped Wotan bargain with the giants Fasolt and Fafner.

At the mention of Loge's name, Fricka exclaimed angrily, "Still you believe in him, after the mischief he has already made!"

"When strength alone is needed, I ask for no help," said Wotan, "but when a situation calls for keenness and cunning, I turn to Loge. He is sure to rescue Freia from the bargain."

"Then where is he now?" asked Fricka.

"And where are my brothers?" asked Freia. Desperately she called their names: "Donner! Froh!"

The tramp of heavy footsteps sounded, and Fasolt and Fafner appeared on the mountaintop. They were huge men dressed in animal skins and carrying heavy wooden staves. For all the roughness of their manner and appearance, they were not without dignity.

Fasolt spoke to Wotan, "While you slept we heaped the heavy stones to build your castle yonder. Now pay us our wage."

"Name your wage," said Wotan.

The giant was puzzled. "We fixed the price beforehand —have you forgotten so soon? It was agreed that we would carry the holy Freia home with us."

"Name another price," said Wotan shortly. "Freia is not for sale."

Fasolt was stunned. "What are you saying! The contract was written on your spear to bind our solemn bargain."

"My trusting brother," said Fafner, "do you not see that he is false?"

Fasolt looked into Wotan's face. "You made a promise."

"It was made in sport," said Wotan. "This goddess is not for such dolts as you."

Fasolt's anger rose. "We giants toiled and sweated to

build your castle so that we might win a fair and gentle woman to brighten our poor lives. Would you break the bond now?"

Fafner stopped him. "Talk will gain us nothing. We must take the goddess by force."

Wotan looked uneasily about for Loge.

The giants were moving toward Freia. "You, there— come with us," ordered Fafner.

Once more Freia cried out for help. This time her cry was answered. Her brothers, Donner and Froh, rushed forward, and Froh clasped Freia in his arms.

Donner, god of thunder, was armed with a hammer. He planted himself before the giants.

"Why do you threaten us?" asked Fafner.

"We want no more than our wage," said Fasolt.

Donner swung his hammer fiercely. "Come here, and I'll pay your wage with a generous hand!"

Wotan stretched his spear between Donner and the giants. "Hold!" he said. "This is not the time for force," and Freia cried in dismay, "He forsakes me!"

But Wotan had only been marking time, waiting for Loge to come to his aid. Now the fire god appeared. He had made his way up from the valley of the Rhine.

"Are you ready to unravel the bad bargain you made?" Wotan asked him.

Loge gave him a look of injured innocence. "What bad bargain? Have not the giants built the castle just as you planned it?"

"Of all the gods, I alone have been your friend," said Wotan. "Would you fail me now? You know I pledged

Freia to the giants only because you promised to save her afterward."

"I promised only that I would *seek* to save her," said Loge.

Fricka said to Wotan, "There is the traitor you have trusted!" and Froh and Donner turned on Loge with curses and insults.

The fire god faced them in defiant scorn. "You place the blame on me to cover your own blunders."

Wotan defended Loge. "Leave him in peace. You do not know his wisdom as I do."

The giants had been waiting impatiently. Now they asked for their wage with no more delay.

Again Wotan tried to prod the fire god to action, and he blamed him for wandering away at a time when the other gods needed him most.

"It was for your sake that I wandered," said Loge, moving shiftily back and forth. "I have been to the ends of the earth in search of a treasure that the giants might accept in place of Freia, but I found none. All the world over, men are agreed that nothing is so precious as a woman's love."

And yet, he went on, he *had* met with one man who had sworn an oath against love. This man was Alberich, the Nibelung. When the Rhinemaidens scorned him, he had stolen their golden treasure, and now he prized it above all else.

Loge appealed to Wotan, "The mourning maidens beg you to help restore the Rhinegold to them. I promised to carry their message to you."

Loge's long, rambling speech had left Wotan wearied and exasperated, but the giants had listened with close attention. They knew Alberich well. He was their sworn enemy, and they begrudged him the stolen gold.

"What gift goes with this treasure?" asked Fafner.

"While the gold lay in the river, it was only a toy," Loge told them, "but shaped into a ring, it can bring mastery of the world to him who holds it."

The giants' eyes grew longing, and there was longing in Wotan's voice when he spoke. "I have heard of this Rhinegold."

Fricka wondered if the gold could not adorn a woman's beauty.

Wotan asked suddenly, "How could I master this treasure? How could I shape it into a ring?"

"You are too late," said Loge. "Alberich has already fashioned the ring, and its power is his."

Donner was alarmed. "Then we are not safe against his power. The treasure must be taken from him."

"And now that it has been shaped into a ring, one need not renounce love to be its master," said Froh.

"Taking the ring would be child's play," said Loge.

"How could it be done?" asked Wotan.

"By theft," said Loge. "What a thief stole must be stolen from the thief. Then the Rhinemaidens may have their gold once more."

But Wotan scoffed at the idea of returning the gold to the Rhinemaidens, and Fricka added, "I care little what happens to that watery brood. They have lured many men to death in the river."

The two giants had been conferring secretly together. Fafner said to Wotan, "You may keep the goddess, Freia. Now we ask in payment only the Rhinegold."

"Are you out of your wits!" cried Wotan. "How can I give you what is not mine?"

"With your cunning and might, you can secure it for us," insisted Fafner.

"For *you* must I do this?" said Wotan indignantly, and he denounced the giants for their greed.

Fasolt's answer was to lunge forward and lay hands on Freia. "We have you now," he said, as she struggled in his grasp. "You must be our pledge until the ransom is paid."

"We shall take her far from here," said Fafner. "At nightfall my brother and I shall come again. If the Rhinegold is not ready—"

He paused, and Fasolt finished, "Then Freia is ours forever."

The giants stalked away, dragging Freia between them.

The other gods looked on in consternation. Loge watched the giants carry Freia down into the valley and across the river.

A mist rose and gradually covered the mountaintop. The gods gazed at one another in fear and dread. In the gray light their faces seemed to be growing haggard and old.

"My hand sinks," said Donner, as the hammer slipped in his grasp.

"My heart stands still," said Froh.

Loge realized what was happening. Without Freia the gods were doomed to grow old and weak and defenseless.

21

Freia alone knew the secret of cultivating the golden apples that grew in her garden. The gods could remain youthful and strong only as long as they ate the apples.

"You ate no fruit from the garden today," said Loge. "Now, with the garden's keeper gone, the apples already begin to spoil on the tree."

As for Loge, he had no need of the fruit. Freia had always kept the apples from him, and so he had learned to live without them, although his strength was only half that of the other gods.

Fricka turned on Wotan. "Your heedlessness has brought us to ruin!"

"Up, Loge," ordered Wotan with sudden resolution. "Off with me to the home of the Nibelungs, and I'll surely seize this gold!"

"Then may the Rhinemaidens hope for a hearing?" asked Loge.

"Silence," said Wotan. "It is Freia who needs our help."

The home of the Nibelungs was underground.

"We shall go by way of the sulphur pit," said Loge. He let himself down through a cleft in the rocks.

Wotan followed Loge into the cleft, and the vapors rose higher until they had covered and darkened all the mountaintop.

SCENE 3

In Nibelheim, underground realm of the Nibelungs, a great cavern stretched away farther than the eye could

22

reach. Smoky flares lighted its walls, and among the rocks were clefts that led to other passageways. The din of hammers clanging on anvils could be heard from all sides.

Once the Nibelungs had worked happily at their anvils, forging trinkets and toys. Now they toiled in slavery. Since Alberich had become master of the Rhinegold, he had made himself master of the gnomes as well. Day after day he forced them to mine gold from the earth and shape the precious metal into bars for his vast and ever-growing hoard.

Alberich entered the cave, dragging his brother, Mime, by the ear. Mime, a shrinking and pathetic little gnome, shrieked in pain and fright.

"Where is the work I ordered?" demanded Alberich. "Weld it for me here on the spot, or I'll nip your ear rarely!"

"The work is done," wailed Mime.

"Then why do you hesitate?" asked Alberich. "Hand it out."

"I feared——" stammered Mime. "I feared—I had failed——"

Alberich had released him. Now he made a motion to seize him again. Terrified, Mime dropped a piece of metal work that he had been concealing in his hand. Alberich snatched it up and examined it.

"This is welded just as I ordered it," he said. "You could not have made it if I had not told you how, and you were trying to deceive me and save this wonderful work for yourself!"

The work was the Tarnhelm, a magic helmet. To test its powers, Alberich set it on his head and spoke the words of a spell. Instantly he vanished in a cloud of smoke.

"Brother, can you see me?" he asked.

Mime asked in bewilderment, "Where are you? I can see you no more."

"Then feel me instead," said the voice of Alberich. "Take this for your thievish tricks," and Mime cringed under the blows of an invisible whip.

Alberich's gloating voice spoke above him, "Thank you, thickhead. Your work is well done."

The cloud of smoke moved out of sight into the back of the cave. From the lower passages came the cries of the gnomes, as Alberich, made invisible by the Tarnhelm, lashed them with his whip.

Mime was left alone. He was still cowering there and moaning in pain when Wotan and Loge descended into the cave.

"This is Nibelheim," said Loge.

"Who lies there groaning?" asked Wotan.

Loge called Mime by name. "What is it that nips and knocks you so?"

"Leave me alone!" said Mime, but when Loge offered him help, the gnome looked up and began to speak. "What help is there for me? My brother, Alberich, has forged a ring of the Rhinegold and through its magic he has made slaves of all his fellow Nibelungs."

He told of the Tarnhelm and how it had come to be made. "I forged it to his exact orders. I guessed that it was enchanted and I wanted to keep it for myself. But Alberich took it from me, and too late I learned that the helmet could make him invisible. He disappeared before my eyes, and now my fool's back is furrowed with stripes."

He rubbed his back and began to moan again, and the gods laughed.

Mime looked at them more closely.

"Who are you?" he asked.

"Friends to you," said Loge. "We are here to free the Nibelungs."

Alberich's scolding voice and the crack of his whip sounded in the distance.

"Look out!" cried Mime. "He is near."

"We'll wait for him here," said Wotan. He quietly seated himself on a stone, and Loge waited beside him.

Alberich came out of the back of the cave. He had taken off the Tarnhelm and placed it in his belt. Shouting and brandishing his whip, he was driving a crowd of Nibelungs up from the caverns below. Their backs were bent under loads of gold and silver that had been fashioned into ornaments of many shapes and sizes. At the master's commands, they piled the metal work into a great, glittering heap.

Alberich saw Wotan and Loge.

"Who is this?" he called out. Quickly he separated Mime from the two strangers and drove him into the midst of the other Nibelungs. "Get below and grub the gold out of the new mines. Whoever is idle will feel the sting of my whip!" He drew the ring from his finger, kissed it, and thrust it commandingly toward the gnomes. "Tremble in terror! Bow to the rule of him who holds the ring!"

With howls and shrieks, the gnomes scattered and disappeared into the crevices of the cave.

Alberich asked Wotan and Loge, "What do you want here?"

Wotan answered mildly, "Strange news has come to us of wonders you have worked. We have come to see these marvels."

"It is only envy that brings you here," said Alberich.

"Is this your thanks to me?" returned Loge. "Have I not given you the fire that brings you light and warmth? Once we were friends. Am I not worthy of your trust?"

"I trust in your falsehoods, not in your truths." Alberich pointed to his hoard of treasure. "Look, that's only for today. Soon I'll have riches enough to win me the world, and you who live in the upper air—I'll grasp and fetter you all!"

As Wotan half rose in anger, Loge said smoothly, "You have indeed worked wonders with your ring, but what if a thief came to steal it while you slept?"

"How delightfully deep is Loge! Always he judges everyone else to be dull," jeered Alberich. "I designed a helmet, and Mime, my most skillful smith, forged it. With the helmet I can take on another form, or I can disappear altogether. So, remaining invisible, I am safe from every-one, even you, my friend!"

"If this were possible, there would be no end to your power," said Loge, "but until I see the proof, I have no faith in such a miracle."

Alberich accepted the challenge. "What shape shall I take on before you?"

"Whatever you choose," said Loge, "but make me dumb with wonder!"

Alberich put on the Tarnhelm. At once he changed to a monstrous serpent that opened its jaws menacingly.

Loge pretended to be frightened out of his wits. "Do not swallow me! Spare poor Loge's life!"

Alberich appeared once more in his own form. He laughed triumphantly. "Now do you believe me?"

"Surely my trembling proves that," answered Loge. "I have seen you take on a larger form, but can you become smaller? It seems to me it would be even more cunning to withdraw from dangers by turning yourself into some-thing as small as a toad."

Without thinking, Alberich fell into Loge's trap.

"Nothing simpler," he boasted. "Look."

In an instant he had turned himself into a toad.

"There!" cried Loge. "Grasp the creature!"

Wotan set his foot on the toad. Loge snatched the Tarnhelm.

With the magic helmet gone, Alberich was once again a gnome, writhing helplessly under Wotan's foot.

Swiftly Loge bound him hand and foot, and the two gods dragged their prisoner to the shaft by which they had entered the cave.

SCENE 4

The mountaintop was still shrouded in mist when Wotan and Loge hauled their captive out of the sulphur pit.

"Look, I beg you," said Loge. "There lies the world which you so longed to bend to your will."

"You scoundrel—you scum!" raged Alberich. "Loosen these bonds and let me go!"

"Before we do that," said Wotan, "a price is due."

"What must I give?" snarled the gnome.

"Your hoard of gold," said Wotan.

"Grasping thieves!" shouted Alberich, but inwardly he was relieved to think this lesson would not be as costly as he had feared. "Untie my hand," he said sullenly.

Loge freed Alberich's right hand. The gnome touched the ring with his lips and muttered a command. "I've called the Nibelungs to bring the hoard from below," he said. "Now untie these ropes."

"Not until we've been paid," said Wotan.

The Nibelungs began to climb up out of the pit, each with a load from the treasure hoard.

"Quick, put the treasure there in a heap, and then be off!" ordered Alberich, galled that his slaves should see him bound and helpless.

The gnomes obeyed and crept meekly back into the pit.

"Now I've paid," said Alberich. "Let me go, and the helmet that Loge holds—have the goodness to give it back."

"This is part of the plunder," said Loge, and he tossed the Tarnhelm on the heap.

Even this was not too crushing a blow to Alberich. Through the power of the ring he could force Mime to forge another helmet. But he said with an air of utter defeat, "Now I lie here stripped of everything. Am I free to go?"

Loge asked Wotan, "Shall I untie him?"

Wotan stood looking down on the gnome. He said deliberately, "On your finger is a golden ring. This must be added to the hoard."

"The ring?" cried Alberich.

Wotan nodded. "It must be ours before you go."

Alberich broke into wild pleading. "Take my life, but not the ring! It is as much a part of me as my eye or ear, my head or hand!"

Wotan was contemptuous. "You call the ring yours,

you impudent earth gnome? Who stole the gold from the Rhinemaidens?"

"Hypocrite!" retorted Alberich. "You yourself would have robbed the Rhinemaidens if you had known the art of forging the gold into a ring!"

"Nothing you say proves *your* right to it," said Wotan, and he tore the ring from Alberich's finger.

While the gnome lay screaming horribly, Wotan put the ring on his own finger and contemplated it with satisfaction. "It is my own," he said to himself, "making me the mightiest ruler of all!"

Loge untied Alberich's bonds.

The gnome began to laugh in insane fury. "Now am I free—really free? Then listen, friends, I curse the ring! May its magic deal death to every owner. May it bring no happiness and no gain till I hold it once more in my hand. You have the ring, but you cannot escape my curse!"

He leaped into the sulphur pit and disappeared.

Undisturbed by Alberich's outburst, Wotan still gazed at the ring.

The mist on the mountain began to clear away. Loge saw the two giants, Fasolt and Fafner, approaching, with Freia following after them.

Fricka, Donner, and Froh appeared on the mountain-top.

"The gods have returned," said Froh, and Fricka asked anxiously, "Have you brought good news?"

Loge pointed to the heap of treasure. "The power of wit has won the prize. There is Freia's price."

As Freia drew near, the air became delightfully fresh and fragrant. The last of the mist faded from the mountaintop, although clouds still hid the distant castle.

The gods breathed deeply, feeling their youthful vigor returning.

Fasolt and Fafner came in sight, with Freia between them. Fricka rushed to greet her sister, but Fasolt motioned her back.

"She is still ours," he said, "until the ransom is paid."

"Here is the ransom—this golden hoard," said Wotan.

Fafner's eyes gleamed, but Fasolt looked on the gold with sadness in his heart. "It grieves me to lose the maiden," he said. "Let the gold be heaped so that it will hide her from sight. It will help me forget her beauty."

"Then find a measure," said Wotan impatiently.

The giants placed Freia before them and thrust their staves into the ground on each side of her in a measure of her height and breadth.

"Hurry with the hateful task," said Wotan, and Loge and Froh began to heap the treasure between the two staves.

Fafner complained that the metal ornaments were being heaped too loosely, and he tried to press them together.

"All these chinks must be closed," he said.

Loge sharply ordered him to take his hands off.

Wotan turned away in shame at this humiliation to Freia, and Fricka reproached him, "See how sad and distressed she stands. It is you who have brought her to this."

Fafner was calling greedily for more treasure.

"This is more than I can bear!" cried Donner. "Come here, you hound, and measure your strength against mine!"

"Quiet, thunderer," sneered Fafner. "No one heeds your rolling here."

Wotan interrupted their quarrel. "Is not Freia completely hidden?"

"I still see the sun shining on her hair," said Fafner. "Throw that metal woven work on the heap."

"What? Even the Tarnhelm?" protested Loge.

"Let it go," said Wotan.

Loge tossed the helmet on top of the heap.

"Then must the lovely Freia be lost to me?" mourned Fasolt. He bent closer to the heap of treasure. "Ah, through this space I can see her eyes. While I gaze on her face, I cannot leave this spot."

"Do you hear?" said Fafner to Loge. "That chink must be closed."

"There is no more treasure," said Loge.

"I see a ring on Wotan's finger," said Fafner. "That will close the space."

"Give up the *ring?*" exclaimed Wotan.

"The gold in this ring belongs to the Rhinemaidens," Loge told the giants. "Wotan means to restore it to them."

But Wotan would not stoop to such a pretense. "What foolish talk is this? The prize was dearly won, and I'll keep it for myself."

"Then my promise to the Rhinemaidens is broken," said Loge.

"Your promise does not bind me," said Wotan.

Fafner was still demanding the ring.

"All the world shall not move this ring from my hand!" declared Wotan.

"Then Freia is ours forever!" Fasolt dragged the goddess from behind the heap of treasure.

Freia called out for help. Fricka, Froh, and Donner implored Wotan to give up the ring.

He stubbornly refused. "The ring is mine."

Fasolt started away with Freia, but Fafner still hoped an agreement might be reached, and he held his brother back.

The light grew dim. The crevice in the mountaintop began to glow with a strange blue radiance, and out of the opening rose the figure of a woman. Her face was noble, her hair was long and black. She was Erda, goddess of earth and wisdom.

She stretched out her hand to Wotan. "Give up the accursed ring. Downfall waits for you in its wealth," she warned him. "Hear me! All that exists comes to an end, and a sad day dawns for the gods."

She sank slowly back into the earth. The glow surrounding her began to fade.

Wotan tried to call her back. "I know there is a secret spell in your words. Tell me more."

"I've warned you now. You know enough," said Erda. "Pause and think on the truth."

She sank out of sight. Wotan rushed to the crevice. "Wait—you must tell me all!"

"Do not try to hold her," begged Fricka, "but listen to her words."

The impetuous Donner said to the giants, "Here, you monsters—Wotan will give you the gold."

"If I dared but hope," said Freia faintly. "Could I be worth such a ransom?"

Wotan had been deep in thought. He spoke at last, "Return, Freia. I set you free," and he threw the ring on the heap of treasure.

The giants released Freia. Joyfully she ran to the gods, and with great rejoicing they embraced her.

Fafner had already spread out a huge sack and was preparing to pack up all the treasure.

Fasolt stopped him. "Greedy one, give me some, too. Surely we should share it equally."

"Since the beginning you cared more for the goddess than the gold," said Fafner. "If it had not been for me, you would not have given her up, so it is right that I keep most of the ransom."

Fasolt appealed to the gods. "Should not the treasure be divided equally?"

"Keep the ring," Loge advised him, "and let him have the rest."

Fasolt threw himself upon his brother, who was busily filling the sack with treasure. Fafner had the ring in his hand. Fasolt snatched at it.

They struggled, and the struggle grew more and more violent, until Fasolt wrested the ring from his brother.

"I have it!" he shouted.

Fafner raised his staff and struck his brother a crushing blow. Fasolt fell, and as he lay dying, Fafner twisted the ring from his hand.

While the gods looked on in horror, Fafner dropped the ring into the sack and coolly gathered up the rest of the treasure.

Loge said to Wotan, "The ring serves you better now that it is lost. See your enemies felling themselves for the gold you have let go?"

Wotan said in a shaken voice, "There is sick fear in my heart. Only Erda can help me. I must go to her."

Fricka moved to his side. "Our castle is waiting. Can we not go there in happiness?"

"A shameful price was paid for this dwelling place," muttered Wotan.

The castle was still hidden by clouds. Weary of the murk and mist, Donner sprang to an overhanging rock and began to swing his hammer, clearing the air with thunder and lightning.

During the storm, Fafner took up his sack of treasure and carried it away, along with the body of Fasolt.

Donner called to his brother, "Let us show what a bridge we can make."

Froh mounted the rock and stood beside Donner. The clouds parted. From the feet of Donner and Froh stretched a rainbow bridge. In dazzling splendor it arched over the valley to the castle, which gleamed in the sunlight.

Froh said to the other gods, "The bridge is light yet strong. It will take you home."

"Night is near. May the castle shelter us now," said Wotan. He took his wife's hand. "Come with me to Valhalla."

"Why do you call the castle by that name?" she asked. "Such a title was never known before."

He answered that as his spirit found strength against its fears, the name would be made clear.

He led her toward the bridge. Froh, Freia, and Donner followed.

Loge paused, meditating as he looked after them. "Even while they hasten to their end, they believe in their everlasting strength. I am ashamed that I must share in what they do."

He moved slowly after the other gods.

Voices rose from the valley of the Rhine: "Give us our gold—give us back our glory!"

"The Rhinemaidens are mourning their lost gold," said Loge.

Wotan had paused at the bridge. "Accursed nixies! Stop their clamor!"

"You in the water—why do you worry us?" called Loge. "You have heard what Wotan wishes."

The Rhinemaidens continued their lament. "Oh, Rhinegold, if only you might shine for us again! All that is good dwells in the waters. Those who are base and bad are enthroned above."

While the maidens lifted their mournful voices, the gods moved out upon the rainbow bridge and crossed toward the castle beyond.

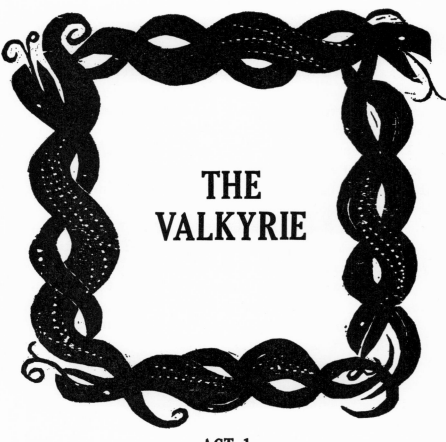

THE
VALKYRIE

ACT 1

ON A WILD and stormy evening a young warrior, lost in
the woods, came upon a hut and took refuge there. Faint
and exhausted, he stopped just inside the doorway and
looked about him. The dwelling was built around a great
ash tree—the trunk and branches grew up through the
roof—and the walls were of rough-hewn boards.

A fire burned in the fireplace, and there was a bearskin

rug in front of the hearth. The man staggered toward the fire and sank down upon the rug.

"Whoever may own this hearth," he said, "here I must rest."

A young woman came out of an inner room. She was Sieglinde, wife of Hunding, who was master of the house. When she saw the stranger, she was astonished but not afraid. She drew near him, trying to guess who he might be. She bent over him to make sure he was breathing.

He lifted his head and called for water.

She hurried out and came back with a drinking horn filled with water. He drank deeply. He nodded his thanks and looked into her face with growing interest.

"The drink has eased both my thirst and my pain," he said. "Who is it who brings me relief?"

She was the wife of Hunding, she told him, and she invited him to stay until her husband returned.

"Wounded and without a weapon," he said, "such a guest will be safe."

Sieglinde said in alarm, "You are wounded? Show me your wounds."

"They are trifles," he answered. "If my shield and spear had been half as strong as my arm, I should never have fled from the foe. But now my shield and spear are broken." His enemies had pressed upon him closely, he told her, but he had outdistanced them. The storm had exhausted his strength. "But now the sun shines on me again," he said.

Sieglinde went to the storeroom and filled a horn with honeyed mead, which she offered him.

"Will you not taste it first?" he asked.

She sipped a little and handed him the horn.

After he had drunk, they were silent for a long time.

He spoke, his voice trembling. "You have cheered a miserable wretch. May no evil reward your kindness. I've rested enough. I'll go my way."

"Why must you go?" she asked.

"Ill fortune follows me. I must not bring it to you." He rose and went to the door.

She called him back. "What curse can you bring to one who lives in an accursed house?"

He gazed searchingly into her face, while she looked down in shy sadness. He came back to the hearth.

He gave her a name by which to call him—Woeful— and he agreed to wait for her husband.

There was another silence, while they looked into each other's eyes.

Steps sounded outside. Sieglinde's husband had returned and was leading his horse to the stable.

She opened the door and Hunding entered. He was a huge man with a somber, forbidding face. He was armed with shield and spear. At the sight of the stranger, he turned to his wife with a coldly inquiring look.

"I found this man exhausted on our hearth," she said.

Hunding asked, "Have you provided for his wants?"

Sieglinde answered that she had.

"She gave me rest and drink," said the stranger. "Should she be blamed for this?"

"My hearth is sacred. You are safe in my house." Hunding's words were gracious, but his manner was sus-

picious and grim. Sieglinde took his weapons and hung them on the trunk of the ash tree, and he ordered her to prepare the evening meal.

She brought food from the storeroom, while Hunding watched her closely, comparing her face with that of the stranger. "How much alike they are!" he said uneasily to himself. "That same gleam comes and goes in their eyes."

He questioned the stranger. What had brought him here? What ill fortune had caused his trouble?

"I came through wood and meadow, storm and stress," said the stranger. "I know nothing of how I came here or where I have wandered."

"You have come to the sheltering roof of Hunding's house," said Hunding. "Now will you make known your name?"

The stranger did not answer. Sieglinde, sitting opposite him across the table, was watching him with sympathy and a strange expectancy.

"If you shrink from telling me," said Hunding ironically, "my wife will listen. See how eagerly she waits."

"No one may call me Peaceful or Joyful," said the stranger. "Woeful is more fitting." He told his gloomy story. He was one of twins, but he had hardly known his sister. Their father was a man named Wolfe, a stalwart man with many enemies. One day he and his father had gone hunting together. They had returned to find their home in ruins. The stranger's mother had been slain, his sister had disappeared.

Sieglinde asked, "Where is your father now?"

"Our enemies pursued us, and in flight I lost all trace

of him," said the stranger. "When I knew that he was gone forever, the woods held no more joy for me. I longed for companionship and love, but wherever I went I was an outcast, and evil followed me."

"How did you come to lose your sword?" asked Sieglinde.

"A maiden asked my help," said the stranger. "Her family would have forced her to marry a man she did not love. I challenged the tyrants and routed them. But when the maid saw her brothers slain, she blamed herself for their death and threw herself upon them, moaning and weeping. The kinsmen burst upon the scene. With sword and shield I defended the maid until the weapons were struck from me, and I fled. And now," he said, "you know why I may not be called Peaceful."

He left the table and moved to the fireplace.

Hunding, too, rose, and he spoke with terrible menace in his voice. "I was called out to avenge the murder of my kinsmen, but I was too late. Now I come home to find the murderer under my own roof. You are my guest. For this night you are safe in my house, but in the morning I will have vengeance!"

Sieglinde had stepped between the two men. Her husband ordered her harshly to go and prepare his night drink and wait for him in the inner room.

Sieglinde went to a cupboard, took out a box, and shook some spices from it into a drinking horn. She climbed the steps to the inner room, and at the door she paused. The stranger was watching her. With her eyes she indicated a particular spot on the trunk of the ash tree.

Hunding gestured toward her with threatening vio-lence. She turned then and carried the drinking horn away into the inner room.

Hunding said to the stranger, "Tomorrow, Wolfe-son, we meet again." He followed Sieglinde into the next room, taking his weapons with him.

Night had come. The stranger sat by the hearth in the light of the dying fire. Bitter and brooding, he recalled his father's promise. "He promised me a sword that I should find in my greatest need. Unarmed, I have fallen into the hands of my enemy, and the woman who fills me with longing is in the power of this cruel tyrant." He called his father's name, "Wälse! Wälse! Where is your sword—the strong sword that will serve me in battle?"

The coals in the fireplace broke apart. A beam of fire-light struck a spot on the tree—the same spot that Sieg-linde had indicated with her eyes. Something gleamed there.

He watched, fascinated and puzzled, until the fire died and the gleam faded.

Sieglinde came out into the room. She was dressed in white, and she moved slowly through the darkness to-ward the stranger.

"Are you asleep?" she asked.

He sprang up in joyful surprise.

"Listen to me," she said. "Hunding is asleep. I placed a drug in his drink. Use the time to save your life." She offered to show him a weapon. "Oh, if only you could use it! It was meant only for the strongest of the strong."

She told him of her wedding day when she became the

44

unwilling bride of Hunding. Among the guests was a strange old man whose hat covered one of his eyes. He looked fiercely at the others, but at her with a yearning kind of tenderness. He carried a sword which he drove into the ash tree. The weapon was to belong to the man who could draw it out. But though one after another tried his strength, no one could move the sword.

"Then I knew who it was who had greeted me in my grief," she said, "and I know, too, for whom the sword is meant. If he would come quickly to my rescue and aid! If I could find the friend and rest in his embrace!"

The stranger took her in his arms. "You have found the friend. Both the weapon and your love I shall win. We have suffered grief and shame, but the day of revenge dawns at last."

Sieglinde started away from him in fright. "Ha! Who went there? Who came in?"

The outside door had swung quietly open. The storm had passed, and it was a glorious spring night. Moonlight poured into the room, and in the sudden brightness the two could see each other clearly.

"No one went, but one has come in," he said. "Spring is here, smiling on us!"

They sat together on a couch. "You are the spring for which I longed," she said, "while winter held me in its embrace. When I first saw you, I knew you were my own." She brushed the hair back from his forehead and looked at him with growing astonishment. "Surely I have seen your face before!"

"In my heart's longing I have seen you, too," he said.

45

"Once I saw my face mirrored in a stream, and now again I see it," she said wonderingly. "And the look in your eyes, I have seen it before—in the look of the old man who eased my sorrow." She asked in a low voice, "Is your name indeed Woeful?"

"Not from this day forward," he said, "now that you love me."

"And you may not truly be called Peaceful?"

"Call me whatever you will," he said.

"Was your father truly called Wolfe?" she asked.

"He was a wolf to fearful foxes," said the stranger, smiling, "but the name he bore was Wälse."

Sieglinde was trembling with excitement. Wälse was *her* father, as well. "If it was for you that he thrust his sword into the tree, let me name you as I would have you!"

Her name for him was Siegmund—Voice of Victory.

"And the victor I will be!" He sprang to the tree and grasped the hilt of the sword. "Love has given me strength to risk bold deeds and death. Nothung—Needful—I'll call you, sword. Show your sharpness, noble steel. Come out of your wooden sheath!"

With a mighty effort, he drew the sword out of the tree.

"Siegmund, the Wälsung, you see here! As a wedding gift he offers the sword, and then he takes you away from the enemy's house."

"If you are Siegmund," she said, "then I am Sieglinde, who has longed for you."

"Both bride and sister be to your brother, then the Wäl-

46

sungs shall flourish forever!" he cried, holding her close in his arms.

ACT 2

Years had passed since the gods' entry into Valhalla. The giant Fafner still held the Rhinegold. With the aid of the magic Tarnhelm he had turned himself into a dragon so that he might better guard the ring. Too dull-witted to comprehend its powers, he spent his days crouching over it in the darkness of a cave.

Alberich, the gnome, from whom the ring had been stolen, waited and watched for a chance to regain the lost treasure.

For all his might and glory, Wotan lived in fear that Alberich might seize the Rhinegold and use it to destroy the gods.

Once Wotan had made a contract with the giants Fafner and Fasolt. The contract was written on the shaft of his spear. By breaking his agreement, he had brought the gods close to disaster. Much as he longed to have the Rhinegold safely in his own hands, he dared not take it from Fafner. His hope was that an earthly hero, independent and free of the gods, might capture the ring.

With a mortal woman, Wotan had founded the family of Wälsungs. He had fathered two children, a son and a daughter. Disguised and calling himself Wolfe or Wälse, he had lived in the woods with his earthly family. He had reared the son, Siegmund, to be fearless and strong—a hero, who might someday win the Rhinegold and bring deliverance to the gods.

With Erda, goddess of earth and wisdom, Wotan had created still another family. Nine daughters, the Valkyries, were born to them.

The Valkyries were warrior maidens. It was their duty to gather the bodies of heroes killed in battle and carry them to Valhalla. There the heroes lived again and helped guard the gods from enemies that threatened them.

Brünnhilde, leader of the Valkyries, was Wotan's favorite daughter. Now she stood with her father near a rocky ravine. He was in full armor, and he carried his spear. She, too, was fully armed.

Wotan ordered her off to the battle between Siegmund and Hunding, who were soon to meet.

"The Wälsung must win," he said, "so up and away!"

The warrior maiden rushed away, happy in the thought of the conflict to come. She leaped from rock to rock, shouting the Valkyries' battle cry, "Ho-jo-to-ho!"

She looked down into the ravine and warned her father to prepare himself for a storm. "Fricka, your wife, is on the way. Though I love the strife of men, I care nothing for domestic wars, so I leave you to your fate!"

Laughing, she hurried out of sight.

Fricka appeared, riding in a chariot drawn by two rams. She alighted and came striding toward Wotan.

"The old storm—the old strife," he sighed. "Yet I must face her!"

She greeted him accusingly. "You were hiding from me. I have had to seek you out to ask your help."

"Speak your troubles freely," he said.

She told him that Hunding had prayed to her for vengeance. "I, guardian of married love, am pledged to punish a brazen pair for their wrong against him."

Wotan defended Siegmund and Sieglinde. The magic of spring had bound them together, he said, and surely love was not a crime.

"How dull and deaf you seem," said Fricka, "as if you did not know a sacred marriage vow has been shamefully broken!"

"The vow is not sacred if it holds two people in a love-less bond," said Wotan.

Fricka denounced him for casting aside the laws he had once honored. Since he had founded the race of Wälsungs, he had neglected his wife for them, and he roamed far and wide with the Valkyries. "Stop at no shame!" she cried. "Let me be crushed in the triumph of wrong!"

Wotan tried to convince her that a hero must come who would defy the laws of the gods and do what no god dared to do.

Fricka was contemptuous. "What worthy deed could heroes do that could not be done by the gods? Your deceit shall not save the Wälsung. It was your power that made Siegmund so brave."

Wotan denied this. "He was reared alone, in sorrow and pain. My shield never sheltered him."

"Then let him stand without a shield," said Fricka. "Take back the sword you gave him."

"Siegmund won the sword in his hour of need," protested Wotan.

"You made the need, and you sent the sword!" said Fricka. "Would you try to deceive me, when I followed your footsteps day and night? For him you thrust the sword into the tree. Can you deny that only your cunning led him where he should find it?"

Wotan could not deny it. He asked sullenly, "What do you ask?"

"That you give up the Wälsung," said Fricka. "That you will not shield him when his avenger calls him to battle."

He avoided her eyes. "I—shall not shield him."

"Let the Valkyrie give him no aid," persisted Fricka.

"She shall be free to choose," said Wotan.

"No, she only obeys your will," said Fricka. "Forbid her to let Siegmund win."

"I cannot!" said Wotan in violent agitation. "He has my sword."

"Then destroy its magic," said Fricka. "Cause it to break in his hand."

Brünnhilde was on her way down from the rocks above, where she had left her horse. As she led the horse down the path, she shouted her battle cry.

Fricka delivered her final word to Wotan. "The Wälsung must die for my honor. Do you pledge your oath?"

Beaten, he flung himself down upon a rocky seat. "Take my oath," he said.

Seeing that Fricka was still there, Brünnhilde had interrupted her battle cry. She came quietly forward and left her horse in a cave beside the path. As Fricka started back to her chariot, the two women met.

"Wotan waits for you. Let him tell you how the lot is

to fall," said Fricka coldly, and she climbed into her chariot and drove away.

Brünnhilde went to her father. Never before had she seen him so disturbed.

"How awful the shame!" he burst out. "I am most wretched of all men!"

Brünnhilde threw down her shield, spear, and helmet and knelt at Wotan's feet. "Father, tell me what ails you. Trust in me. See, Brünnhilde begs you!"

Speaking more quietly, Wotan began to tell her of his past—how, when love's young illusions faded, he longed for power. He told her how Loge, the fire god, had helped

him take the Rhinegold from Alberich, the Nibelung, and how Erda had warned him against the ring. "With you Valkyries I sought to escape the doom she prophesied," he said. "To make us strong in battle with the enemy I sent you in search of heroes."

"And we have filled your hall with heroes," said Brünnhilde, "so why should you be afraid?"

Wotan told her of his fear that the Rhinegold might fall into the hands of Alberich. A hero was needed with the strength and courage to take the ring from Fafner, but this hero must act of his own free will.

At once Brünnhilde thought of Siegmund. "Is he not free?"

Wotan confessed miserably that Siegmund's will was not free. "All my cunning could not conceal it. Fricka found out the truth and filled me with shame. Try as I would, I could not resist her."

"Then Siegmund is doomed to defeat?" asked Brünnhilde.

"The curse of Alberich's gold still clings to me. I must abandon what I love," answered Wotan. "Soon will your glory be ended." Word had come to him that Alberich had won a woman who was greedy for gold. To the loveless pair a child would be born, and Erda had foretold that when this happened the reign of the gods would come to an end. Wotan lifted his voice in helpless fury, "Take my blessing, then, son of the Nibelung! May you inherit all I hate!"

Brünnhilde was frightened. "Tell me quickly, what must I do?"

52

"Go fight for Fricka," said her father. "What she has chosen I must choose, too."

Brünnhilde implored him to take back his words. "You love Siegmund. For your sake I'll shield him!"

Her show of defiance roused Wotan to fearful rage. "What are you but the willing, blind tool of my power? Siegmund must fall!"

He stalked away and disappeared among the rocks.

Brünnhilde took up her weapons. "They weigh me down," she said mournfully to herself, "yet how light they seemed when I bore them willingly. Woe, my Wälsung! In your time of need, I must forsake you."

She saw Siegmund and Sieglinde in the ravine below. She watched them for a little while, then she stepped into the cave in which she had left her horse.

Siegmund and Sieglinde came up out of the ravine. She would have hurried on, but he held her there and ordered her to rest.

She threw her arms about him. The next moment she started wildly away. Since leaving Hunding, she had had time to reflect. Remorse and terror overwhelmed her.

"Leave me, an outcast! Never call me your bride," she cried, "lest I bring shame to you!"

"The blood of your foe will pay for the shame you have suffered," said Siegmund. "Wait here for his coming, and I shall surely slay him."

The sound of horns told Sieglinde that Hunding was on his way to avenge the disgrace to his house. Terrified and exhausted, she fainted in Siegmund's arms.

He lowered her gently and seated himself so that her

head rested against his knee. He bent over her and kissed her forehead.

Brünnhilde came out of the cave, leading her horse. She gazed earnestly at Siegmund before she spoke.

"Look on me. Soon you will follow me."

He looked up in surprise. "Who are you? You are beautiful, though you seem strange."

"Only the doomed know my glance," she said. "On the field of death alone I come to heroes."

He reflected on her words. He asked, "Where do you lead the heroes?"

"To Wotan, in Valhalla," she answered.

"Does he live there alone?" asked Siegmund.

"Great bands of fallen heroes will greet you there," she said.

"In Valhalla shall I find my father, Wälse?" he asked.

"He will be found there," she told him.

"Will a woman greet me in Valhalla?" he asked.

He would find a host of wish maidens, she said. Wotan's daughter herself would fill his cup.

"And Sieglinde?" he asked. "Will she be there, too?"

Brünnhilde answered that this could not be.

"Then greet for me Valhalla and Wotan and Wälse and all the heroes and maidens," he said. "I shall not go with you."

"You must go," she said. "You will be slain by Hunding."

Siegmund showed her his sword. "Do you know this? He who made it wills that I shall win."

"He who made it now dooms you to death. He has

54

taken the spell from the sword." Brünnhilde had raised her voice.

"Be still," he said, "and do not disturb the slumberer here." He bent tenderly over Sieglinde and vowed never to forsake her.

Brünnhilde said in agitation, "Do you care so little for heavenly bliss? Is nothing sacred to you but that poor, weak woman who rests on your knee?"

Siegmund answered bitterly, "So young and fair you seem, yet how cold and hard your heart must be. Go and leave me alone and waste no more words on the hateful joys of Valhalla."

Moved by the depth of his love, Brünnhilde offered to shelter and care for Sieglinde.

"None but me shall shelter her," said Siegmund. "If I must die, this sword shall slay my bride before she wakes."

Brünnhilde pleaded that Sieglinde must be spared for the sake of the child she was to bear.

Siegmund drew his sword and spoke to it. "Two lives lie before you, Nothung. Take them in one swift stroke."

Brünnhilde could bear no more. "Hold, Wälsung! Hear me. The death doom is recalled. I bring life to Sieg-mund and Sieglinde. Trust to your sword and strike without fear. Farewell, bravest of men, until we meet on the field of battle!"

She rushed away with her horse. Siegmund looked after her with joy and elation.

Heavy clouds had begun to darken the sky. The horn calls of Hunding and his men had grown louder.

Sieglinde was resting peacefully. Was it the kindness

of the Valkyrie, Siegmund wondered, that had brought her this merciful sleep? He put her gently down upon the rocks.

The horns sounded again. Siegmund drew his sword and hurried up the path until the clouds hid him from sight.

Sieglinde lay where he had left her. A troubled dream disturbed her rest. Lightning flashed, and a crash of thunder awakened her. She leaped to her feet.

From the rocky pass behind her came the voice of Hunding: "Traitor! Stand and give battle!"

The voice of Siegmund answered him defiantly.

In a flash of lightning, Sieglinde saw Hunding and Siegmund fighting in the pass.

She shrieked and started toward them. Another flash of lightning blinded her, and in its glare, Brünnhilde appeared, flying about Siegmund and protecting him with her shield.

"Strike, Siegmund!" cried the Valkyrie. "Trust in your sword!"

Siegmund aimed a deadly blow at Hunding. Before he could strike, a reddish glow broke through the clouds, and Wotan was there, standing over Hunding.

Brünnhilde recoiled in horror.

Wotan stretched out his spear, and Siegmund's sword was shattered against it.

Hunding thrust his sword into Siegmund's breast. Sieglinde heard his death groan, and she fell fainting upon the rocks.

The glow vanished. Brünnhilde came out of the darkness, leading her horse. She lifted Sieglinde into the saddle and disappeared with her into the cave.

The clouds parted and revealed Hunding as he drew his sword from Siegmund's breast. Wotan stood behind him, gazing somberly down on Siegmund's body.

He spoke to Hunding, "Go, slave, and kneel to Fricka. Tell her Wotan's spear avenged that which brought her shame."

He gestured with his hand—a gesture of contempt and loathing—and Hunding fell dead.

Suddenly he burst into a terrible rage at the thought of Brünnhilde's disobedience. "Woe to her! She shall pay for her crime if my horse overtakes her in flight!"

ACT 3

The Valkyries had agreed to meet on a mountaintop, after gathering the bodies of heroes slain in battle. Four of the maidens—Gerhilde, Ortlinde, Waltraute, and Schwertleite—had already gathered.

Lightning flashed and clouds streamed by, and out of the storm came four more Valkyries—Helmwige, Siegrune, Grimgerde, and Rossweisse. Each came soaring through the air on horseback, and across the saddle of each was the body of a warrior.

They left their horses in the nearby wood and joined the other maidens.

"Let us go to Valhalla," said Rossweisse. "Wotan waits for the slain heroes."

But Brünnhilde was missing.

"We must wait for her," said Waltraute. "Our father would be angry if we should come without her."

Siegrune, who had climbed to the rocks above, called that Brünnhilde was in sight. Mounted on her horse, Grane, she was racing furiously through the storm.

The others climbed to the lookout.

"What does she carry on her saddle?" asked Ortlinde.

"That is no man," said Helmwige, and Siegrune said, "It is a maid!"

Brünnhilde rode into the wood, and her sisters ran to meet her. When they returned, she was with them, supporting and leading Sieglinde.

"I am pursued!" Brünnhilde told the others. "The War Father hunts me down!"

Swiftly she told of Siegmund and Sieglinde and confessed that she had disobeyed her father.

Brünnhilde's horse was exhausted. She asked her sisters to lend her another mount. They refused, fearing to risk Wotan's wrath.

Sieglinde had been gazing numbly before her. She spoke now, "Suffer no sorrow for me. Death is my due," and she prayed that Brünnhilde would now strike her dead.

"Live for the love that awaits you," said Brünnhilde. "You bear a Wälsung's life."

Sieglinde thought of the child she was to bear, and her face lighted with sudden joy. "Rescue me—guard me!" she cried.

Wotan was fast drawing near.

"Wrath threatens this woman," said Brünnhilde's sisters. "We dare not give her shelter."

Brünnhilde told Sieglinde with resolution, "You must fly quickly and alone. While my father's wrath falls on me, you may escape." She asked her sisters, "Which of you has traveled to the east?"

Siegrune answered, "To the east is the dense forest where Fafner guards the Nibelung's treasure."

Schwertleite said, "The giant is changed to a dragon, and in a cave he guards Alberich's ring."

"It is no haven for a hapless woman," said Grimgerde.

And yet, said Brünnhilde, Sieglinde might hide safely there, because Wotan shunned the place.

Waltraute called from the lookout that Wotan was near.

From under the breastplate of her armor Brünnhilde took the pieces of Siegmund's sword, which she gave to Sieglinde. "Keep them for Siegmund's son. By good fortune I saved them from the battlefield. Someday he shall wield the weapon, and now I declare his name to be Siegfried, Son of Victory!"

Sieglinde gave fervent thanks to Brünnhilde. With renewed strength and courage, she hastened away.

Thunderclouds enveloped the peak, and out of the storm Wotan called Brünnhilde's name.

She turned to her sisters for help, and they gathered about her, hiding her in their midst. Wotan came out of the wood. In a terrible voice he demanded Brünnhilde.

The other Valkyries pleaded with him to soften his anger toward her.

"Weak-spirited, womanish brood, such melting moods never came from me!" he berated them. "I steeled you to bear hardships and distress, and now you moan and groan when my wrath falls on a traitor. Do you know what she has done? She defied my will, scorned my sacred command. Do you hear, Brünnhilde? Do you think that by shrinking from me you escape your doom?"

Brünnhilde came forward. She walked humbly yet firmly. Within a short distance of Wotan she stopped.

"Here I stand, Father," she said, "to suffer my sentence."

"I do not sentence you. You have shaped the sentence for yourself," said Wotan. "It was my will that gave you life. You have defied that will. Once you were a Valkyrie. Henceforth remain merely what you are."

"Do you disown me?" asked Brünnhilde.

"You shall ride no more from Valhalla, mingle no more with the gods," said Wotan. "Our bond is broken, and you are exiled and banished forever."

Brünnhilde was incredulous. "You will take from me all you have given?"

"He who wins you will take it away," said Wotan. "Here on this rock I banish you. Here you shall sleep, with no defense against any man who shall find you and wake you."

Brünnhilde's sisters cried out against the terrible sentence.

Wotan silenced them. "Did you not hear what I decreed? Your sister is banished from among you. No more shall she ride through the air with you. She shall fail and fade. She shall know a man for her master and sit at home and spin, a mark of scorn for all free spirits!"

Brünnhilde sank to the ground. Her sisters drew back.

"Do you fear her doom?" cried Wotan. "Then flee from the outcast and come to this rock no more. Leave her to bear her sentence alone."

The Valkyries fled in confusion.

The storm died. The light of a calm evening filled the sky.

Brünnhilde still lay at her father's feet. Slowly she raised herself until she was kneeling before him.

"Was it so shameful, what I have done?" she asked. "Was my sin so great that you should rob me of honor forever? In defending Siegmund, I obeyed your own command."

"But I withdrew my command," he said.

"Only because Fricka forced you to be false to yourself," said Brünnhilde.

Wotan was no longer angry. He admitted the truth of her words. Still, she had defied him. She must accept her punishment.

Must she be punished, she asked, even though she had given aid to the Wälsungs, from whom a hero might yet rise?

"Leave the Wälsungs in peace," said Wotan in bitter sadness. "As you are lost to me, so are they."

"Sieglinde guards the sword that was made for Siegmund," said Brünnhilde.

"That sword I struck into splinters," said her father. "Do not seek to change me. I have stayed here too long.

Now I must deal your punishment." She must lie asleep and helpless, to be the wife of the man who awakened her. This was Wotan's decree.

"Shall I fall prey to any worthless man?" she asked. "One thing I beg—that you surround me with horrors, so that only a fearless one will find me here."

"You ask too much," he said.

Brünnhilde clasped his knees and broke into a wild lament.

Wotan was deeply moved. He lifted her to her feet and looked into her face. Shaken with grief, he promised to grant her wish. He kissed her eyes, and she sank into a deep sleep. He laid her gently down upon a moss-covered bank.

He closed the helmet over her face and covered her with her shield.

He pointed his spear at a great stone. "Listen and heed!" he called to Loge, the fire god. "Appear with your fire!"

Three times he struck the rock with his spear. A stream of fire leaped from the stone and surrounded him. He directed the flames with his spear until they rose and encircled the mountaintop.

He spoke the words of a spell, "He who fears my spear point's sharpness shall never pass through these flames."

For the last time he looked at Brünnhilde. Then he walked away through the fire.

SIEGFRIED

ACT 1

MIME, THE GNOME, was busy at his anvil. In the gloom of his forest cave he worked, beside the great forge that stood against the wall.

Hunched over the huge anvil, he looked smaller and more shrunken than ever. He was hammering out a sword. More and more slowly he worked, until at last he stopped in utter dejection. This sword was the strongest he could make, yet he knew it would be only a toy in the hands of the boy for whom it was intended.

He threw it down upon the anvil. There *was* a blade the boy could not shatter, he reflected—the one called Nothung, or Needful. But that sword was broken, and with all his Nibelung skill he could not mend it.

"If I were cunning enough to put it together," he said to himself, "I should be well paid for my pains."

Not far away lived the giant Fafner. In the form of a dragon he guarded the Rhinegold and the rest of the treasure hoard that had once belonged to Alberich, the Nibelung. A thought had taken shape in Mime's brain: "Someday the boy might prove strong enough to take the Rhinegold from Fafner. Then I'd have it for myself!"

The boy was Siegfried, son of Siegmund and Sieglinde. After Siegmund's death, Sieglinde had fled to the forest, where she died giving birth to her son.

Mime had reared the child, who was now a young man, boisterous and brave and a trial to his foster parent.

Sighing and complaining, the gnome went back to his work.

Siegfried burst into the cave. He was a powerfully built young man, wearing the rough clothes of a forester and carrying a silver horn on a chain. He had caught a large bear in the woods and was leading it by a rope.

Mime scurried behind the forge.

"Come—bite him, bite him!" shouted Siegfried, and he pushed the bear toward Mime.

"Take him away!" squeaked the gnome. "Why do you bring the bear in here?"

"Bruin, ask for the sword," said Siegfried.

"There is the sword, finished and ready!" cried Mime.

"Then you've saved your skin for today." Siegfried took the rope off the bear. "Run along, Bruin. Your business here is done," and the bear trotted back into the woods.

Mime came trembling from behind the forge. "It is well enough when you slay the bears, but why do you bring them here alive?"

"Because they are better companions than you." Siegfried started toward the anvil.

Mime handed him the sword. "I've made it sharp. You'll be pleased with its brightness."

"What good is its brightness if its steel is not hard and true?" Siegfried tested the blade with his hand. "Hey, do you call this silly switch a sword?" He beat the blade to pieces on the anvil, shouted in rage at Mime, and threw himself down upon a stone seat.

The gnome had retreated to a safe distance. "Always ungrateful! If everything's not of the best, all the good things I make are quickly forgotten. You should think kindly of Mime, who always shows kindness to you."

Sulkily Siegfried turned his back to the gnome.

Mime offered him broth and roasted meat. Siegfried knocked the food out of his hands.

"This is my reward for all I've done for you," wailed Mime. "I kept you warm and gave you food and shelter. I made you toys and taught you crafts and wisdom, and all you give me in return is hate and abuse."

Siegfried turned and looked searchingly into Mime's face. Mime could not meet his gaze.

66

"You have taught me many things, but never have you taught me to endure the sight of you," said Siegfried. "When I turn my eyes on you, I see evil. When you shake and shamble and slink and shrink, I long to take you by the neck and put an end to you forever! And yet—when I leave you and wander in the forests, why do I always come back to you?"

"My son," said Mime in unctuous tones, "this shows you how close I am to your heart."

Siegfried laughed scornfully. "I cannot even endure you!"

Mime insisted that the feeling must be love. "What the father is to the young bird, so am I to you."

"Since you're so clever, explain this to me," said Siegfried. "You once told me that birds were husband and wife. They nested and brought forth young and both took care of their brood. I saw the deer go in pairs, and wolves and foxes and bears, and together they cared for their young, and for the first time I learned what love must be. Where is your wife, that I may call her Mother?"

Mime was confused and angry. "Are you a fool? Are you either a bird or a beast?"

"Does that mean I never had a mother?" asked Siegfried.

"Only trust what I tell you," said Mime. "I am your father and mother in one."

"You lie!" said Siegfried. "The young is like the parent, and you and I are no more alike than a toad and a fish. Now I know why I always come back to you. It is because you alone can tell me who my father and mother are."

67

He caught the gnome by the throat. "Tell me, rascally knave, who are my father and mother?"

Mime had no choice but to answer. He began to tell of the weeping woman he had found long ago in the forest. He had brought her to this cave, where her child was born. "She died, but Siegfried lives," and he interrupted his tale with reminders of how tenderly he had cared for the helpless babe.

"You've said that before," said Siegfried. "Tell me now who gave me my name."

"Your mother so named you," answered Mime.

"What was my mother's name?"

Mime recalled that the woman's name was Sieglinde.

"And my father's name?"

This the gnome did not know.

Siegfried challenged the story. "If you have not lied as usual, let me see a sign."

Mime hesitated, then brought forth a broken sword. "This your mother gave me—small payment for my toil and trouble. She said your father carried it in the fight in which he died."

"This is my rightful sword!" exclaimed Siegfried. "You shall forge the pieces. Hurry, Mime, and if I find a flaw in the steel, I'll baste your hide. This day I'll have my own weapon!"

The gnome was bewildered and frightened. "Why must you have the sword today?"

"So I can go out into the world and never come back. You are not my father. This is not my home. There is nothing to keep me here!" And Siegfried rushed away.

Mime was in a panic. How could he hope to seize the Rhinegold from Fafner without Siegfried's help? And how could he mend the stubborn steel of the sword, Nothung?

He sank down on his stool behind the anvil.

Out of the woods came a Wanderer—the god Wotan in disguise. He was a tall figure in a long dark cloak. He carried his spear as a staff, and he wore a large hat which he kept pulled low so no one could see that one of his eyes was missing. He entered through an opening in the back of the cave. "Hail, most wise smith!" he greeted Mime.

The gnome was startled. "Who seeks me out here?"

"The world calls me Wanderer," answered the god. "I've roamed the world at will."

"Then roam on your way and do not rest here," said Mime.

The Wanderer came nearer. "Good men welcome me. Much I've questioned, and much I've learned. My wisdom has kept many from woe and sorrow."

"I have wisdom enough," said Mime ungraciously. "I want no more."

The Wanderer sat down by the hearth. "My head is yours," he said, "if I cannot answer any question you ask."

Mime was eager to be rid of the stranger as quickly as possible, and he agreed to ask three questions. He asked first, "What race lives in the deepest caves of the earth?"

"The Nibelungs," answered the Wanderer. "Alberich ruled them all through the spell of a magic ring."

"What race lives here on the earth's broad back?" asked Mime.

"The giants," answered the Wanderer. "Fasolt and Fafner were their rulers. They won Alberich's treasure hoard and the ring besides. There was strife between the two, and Fasolt fell. Now Fafner, as a dragon, holds the hoard."

Mime asked his final question. "What race lives on the cloud-covered heights?"

"There live the gods, and Valhalla is their hall," answered the Wanderer. "Wotan rules there. From a branch of the sacred ash he made a spear shaft on which the holiest treaties of the world are written. With this for a scepter, he rules the world." As if by accident, he let his spear rest on the ground, and a peal of thunder sounded.

Mime said fearfully, "You have won both your head and the wager. Be on your way now."

"You offered me an unfriendly welcome," said the Wanderer. "To gain a place at your hearth I gave my head into your hands. Now your own head is at stake. Answer me three times, or forfeit your life."

Mime was cowed into submission by the stranger's commanding words and bearing. Trembling, he waited.

"What is the race that Wotan treats most harshly yet loves more than his life?" asked the Wanderer.

"The Wälsungs," answered Mime. "Siegmund and Sieglinde sprang from the race. Siegfried is their son."

The Wanderer asked his second question. "A wily Nibelung has brought up Siegfried, fated slayer of Fafner, so that he may take the ring and the treasure hoard for himself. With what sword must Siegfried strike to slay this Fafner?"

"Nothung is the sword," said Mime eagerly, forgetting how he had figured in the question. "It was thrust into an ash tree by Wotan, and only the strongest hero could draw it out. It was Siegmund who won it. Then it was broken against Wotan's spear. Now a cunning smith keeps the pieces, knowing well that with Wotan's sword the bold and foolish Siegfried will slay the dragon."

The Wanderer complimented him on his wit. "And for the third question, tell me whose hand will mend the sword Nothung?"

Mime rose up in terror. "Alas, what shall I do? Accursed steel—if only I had not stolen it! Who'll forge the steel I cannot forge? Who'll teach me the secret?"

The Wanderer had risen from the hearth. "Three questions you asked me. All three I answered. Yet what was nearest your heart you did not ask. Now that I've found out, you are frightened. I've won your head. Hear now and heed, luckless gnome. He who has never learned to fear will make Nothung new. Guard your head well. I forfeit it to this fearless man."

He left the cave and disappeared into the forest.

Mime sank onto his stool. He was weak and trembling. His mind was filled with morbid fears.

Siegfried called from outside, "Ho there, idler! How is it with the sword?"

The gnome shrieked and collapsed behind the anvil.

When Siegfried stepped inside the cave, he saw no one. "Where are you?" he shouted. "Where are you hiding?"

"Is it you, boy?" asked Mime in a quavering voice.

"Under the anvil!" said Siegfried, laughing at the

ridiculousness of the gnome's position. "What are you doing there? Is my sword ready yet?"

Mime recalled the Wanderer's words—that only one who had never learned to fear could make the sword new. The thought came to him: perhaps Siegfried was the one.

He began to speak of fear.

The word was new to Siegfried. "If fear is an art, why did you not teach me? Tell me, what is fear?"

Mime launched into a harrowing description. "In a gloomy forest, with a storm coming on, have you never felt all your senses sink and forsake you? Unless you have had these feelings, you have not known fear."

These feelings seemed strange and interesting to Siegfried. He wanted to know them. "Can you bring it about?" he asked.

The gnome answered that he had thought of a way. "I know a dragon that has slain many men. Follow me to his cave, and you'll learn fear."

"Where is his cave?" asked Siegfried.

"East, at the end of the wood," said Mime.

"And is not the world in that direction?" asked Siegfried.

"The cave is close to the world," Mime told him.

"Take me to learn about fear," ordered Siegfried, "and forth to the world. Quick, shape the sword, so that I may swing it in the world!"

Forging the blade was too great a task for his skill, answered Mime. "Perhaps one who never felt fear could grasp the art more quickly," he suggested.

"Bring me the pieces, you bungler. I'll forge the blade

myself!" Siegfried threw charcoal onto the fire. He fixed
the pieces of the sword in Mime's vise and began to file
them to powder.

"What are you doing? Why do you spoil the steel so?"
protested Mime, yet he knew in his heart that Siegfried's
mighty will would achieve his purpose.

"Unless Fafner teaches him fear, my head will go to
Siegfried," muttered the gnome. "And if Siegfried learns
fear, he cannot conquer Fafner, and I will still be without
the ring! What shall I do? How can I deal with the boy!"

"Mime, quick!" said Siegfried. "Tell me the name of
the sword."

"Nothung—Needful—is its name, so your mother
said," Mime told him.

"Nothung! Nothung! Wonderful sword!" sang Siegfried, and he blew the fire with the bellows.

By this time it was clear to Mime that Siegfried would
mend the sword, slay Fafner, and take the ring and the
treasure hoard. But then would not Siegfried slay Mime?
How could Mime save his head and at the same time gain
the prize?

Out of his feverish plotting came a plan. Siegfried
would be thirsty after his fight with the dragon. Mime
would have a drink ready to offer him, a drink containing
a sleeping potion. Afterward, while Siegfried slept, he
should be slain with his own sword!

In gleeful anticipation, Mime began to skip about the
cave, fetching spices and herbs and shaking them into a
cooking pot.

Siegfried had blown up the fire until the steel in the

crucible was molten. He poured it into a mold and plunged the mold into the water trough. The water hissed and steamed as the steel cooled.

At the other end of the hearth, Mime had put his brew on the fire.

"The craftsman has turned to cooking," said Siegfried derisively. He broke the mold, laid the glowing steel on the anvil, and began to hammer it. Again he plunged it into the water, then he began to fit it into a handle.

Meanwhile, Mime's brew was finished, and he saw the Nibelung ring and the treasure hoard within his grasp. The despised gnome would be master of all. Men and gods would do his bidding while he toiled no more!

Siegfried had been shaping the sword with a small hammer. He spoke to the sword as if it were a living thing. "What once was shattered I have made anew. No stroke shall ever destroy you. Once you lay dead, but I have given you life again!"

He lifted the blade high. With a single blow he split the great anvil in two.

Mime fell to the ground in sudden terror, while Siegfried shouted exultantly and brandished the sword.

ACT 2

Alberich, brother of Mime, crouched in the darkness outside Fafner's cave. A wind sprang up, a light gleamed in the forest, and he listened and watched, wondering if the dragon's slayer might be approaching.

Long ago Alberich had taken the Rhinegold from the Rhinemaidens and forged it into a ring. Wotan and the fire god, Loge, had robbed him of it. Now it was in Fafner's grasp, but Alberich had never given up hope of regaining his lost prize.

The wind died, the gleam faded, and the Wanderer came out of the forest. Moonlight broke through the clouds and lighted his face, and Alberich recognized him as the god Wotan.

Fury overcame his awe. "Begone, you shameless thief!" he cried.

The Wanderer greeted him sardonically. "Black Alberich, are you guarding Fafner's house?"

"Are you spreading new evil?" returned Alberich.

"I am here as witness, not as worker," said the Wanderer.

Alberich denounced him as a vile and treacherous trickster. "I know your wiles, and now I know your weakness. My treasure and my ring paid your debt to the giants who built Valhalla. Your promises to them are written on the shaft of your spear, and you dare not steal back what you paid, or your heavenly staff would crumble like dust!" He warned the Wanderer, "Let the ring come into my hand again, and I'll not be like the stupid giants. I'll use its great might and storm Valhalla's towers."

The Wanderer remained calm. "The true master of the ring will win it himself," he said.

"What of the young man of your own blood?" asked Alberich. "Have you not fostered him in the hope that he will win the prize the gods dare not grasp?"

"Quarrel with Mime, not with me," said the Wanderer. "Soon he will come here bringing a youth who knows nothing of the ring or of me. He is serving your brother's need, so do your work as you will."

Alberich asked eagerly, "You will not try to seize the treasure?"

"The youth will stand or fall with no help from me," the Wanderer assured him.

"I have only Mime to fight for the ring?" asked Alberich.

"Only you and Mime covet the gold," said the Wanderer.

Alberich asked for even more reassurance. "Then I shall make the treasure mine?"

The Wanderer told him, "A hero is on his way to rescue the gold. Two Nibelungs are greedy for it. Fafner is doomed to die. The gold will then belong to him who seizes it. Would you hear more? There lies Fafner. Warn him his death is near. He may give you the toy. I'll waken him for you, myself."

He called into the cave, while Alberich looked on, astonished and expectant.

From the depths of the cave came Fafner's hollow voice, "Who wakes me from sleep?"

"Here stands a friend to warn you of danger," the Wanderer called back.

Alberich stood beside the Wanderer on the knoll in front of the cave. He, too, called to the dragon. "Wake, Fafner! A mighty hero comes to test his strength against yours."

"My hunger is keen," answered Fafner.

"He seeks the ring alone," said Alberich. "Give it to me, and there shall be no fight, and the rest of the treasure shall be yours."

"I hold what I have. Let me slumber," yawned the dragon.

The Wanderer laughed aloud. "That stroke failed. Listen to my counsel and heed it well. All things go by their natures, and fate may not be changed. I leave you to contend with your brother, Mime."

Accompanied by a storm and a gleam of light, he disappeared into the forest.

Alberich cursed the gods, and he stepped out of sight into a rocky cleft, where he could wait and listen.

Morning was breaking. Mime and Siegfried came out of the forest and stopped before the cave. Siegfried wore the sword Nothung in his belt.

"We've reached the place," said Mime.

Siegfried sat down under a lime tree. "Is it here that I shall learn fear?" he asked. "I've journeyed all night with you, Mime, and now you must leave me. If I do not learn about fear in this place, I'll travel on alone."

The gnome pointed to the cave. There lived the horrible dragon, he said. With a snap of his jaws the dreadful creature could swallow a man. The venom of this monster was a deadly poison. His tail had the bone-crushing strength of a mighty serpent.

Siegfried asked if the dragon had a heart.

"A fierce, ruthless heart," said Mime.

"Then Nothung will pierce him through the heart,"

said Siegfried. "Is this all you have to teach me? Be on your way. I'll not learn fearing from you."

"Wait until you see the dragon. Then all your senses will swoon," said Mime. "You will know fear, and you will thank the one who brought you here and think how Mime loves you."

"Get out of my sight and leave me alone," ordered Siegfried. "I can stand no more of your talk of love. When shall I have done with your slinking and blinking?"

The gnome meekly agreed to go, but only as far as the nearby spring. "Stay here, and when the sun is at its height, the dragon will pass this spot on his way to drink from the stream." He added, "When you are faint from the fight and need refreshment, will I not be welcome?"

Siegfried drove him away, and the gnome said darkly as he went, "Fafner and Siegfried. Siegfried and Fafner. If only they might kill each other!"

Siegfried stretched out in the shade of the great lime tree. With Mime gone, the woods seemed fresh and beautiful. All about him was the quiet murmuring of the forest.

Lost in a reverie, he thought of his mother. What had she had been like, and why had she had to die? Did every human mother die when her child was born?

Through the forest murmurs came the song of a bird. He listened, feeling that in the music there might be a message for him if only he could understand. Perhaps the bird might even tell him of his mother.

An idea came to him. He would listen to the song and play the notes on a reed. Then the message might become clear.

He cut a reed with his sword and fashioned it into a pipe.

But when he tried to imitate the bird's song on the pipe, the sounds he made were shrill and out of tune.

He threw the pipe away. If he could not follow the notes of the bird, he could at least play a song of his own. He began to play the silver horn he carried. Often before he had blown his loud and lusty calls in the hope that they would bring him a companion.

Fafner wakened and came creeping ponderously out of his cave. He was a monstrous, lizardlike dragon with a scaly body and a flat, evil-looking head. He dragged himself forward until his forefeet rested on the knoll in front of the cave. There he stopped, peering and yawning.

Siegfried stared at the creature, and suddenly he burst out laughing to think what a lovely companion his song had brought him!

"What is there?" asked Fafner in a strange, hollow voice.

"So you are a beast that can speak," said Siegfried. "Perhaps you can teach me something. I've never learned to fear. Can I learn from you?"

"Are you overbold?" asked the dragon.

"I do not know," answered Siegfried, "but you shall feel my sword unless you can teach me the meaning of this fear."

The dragon laughed harshly. "I came for a drink, and now I find food!" He opened his jaws and showed his teeth.

"This is truly a dazzling sight," observed Siegfried.

"You had better close the cavern; your gullet gapes too wide."

"It opens to eat you," said the dragon.

Siegfried drew his sword and sprang forward. The dragon spat venom from his nostrils. He tried to encircle Siegfried with his tail.

Siegfried avoided both these attacks. He leaped over the dragon and wounded him in the tail.

Fafner bellowed in pain. He tried to throw himself upon Siegfried. As he lifted himself, his breast was exposed. Swiftly Siegfried drove his sword into Fafner's heart.

The great body of the dragon heaved convulsively. Siegfried let go of the sword and moved aside.

The dying Fafner looked at Siegfried, not with hatred, but in a bewildered kind of wonder. "Who are you, brave youth?" he asked. "Who led you to this murder?"

Siegfried answered that he did not know much, not even who he was, but he believed it was Fafner alone who had stirred him to fight.

"You bold, bright-eyed boy, you must know who I am," said the dragon. "The giants Fasolt and Fafner both have fallen. For the cursed gold paid us by the gods I killed Fasolt. Now, as a dragon defending the hoard, Fafner, the last of the giants, is slain. Listen well, bold one. He who drove you to this deed is plotting death for you."

Fafner raised himself, sighed deeply, and fell dead. Siegfried drew his sword from the dragon's body. A few drops of blood fell upon his hand and burned like fire. Involuntarily he put his hand to his mouth.

The forest bird was singing overhead. Siegfried listened, hardly breathing. Tasting the dragon's blood had given him the power to understand the birds' language. The bird was speaking to him!

"Hei!" sang the bird. "Siegfried now owns all the Nibelung's hoard that lies hidden in the cave. If he should win the Tarnhelm, it would serve him for deeds of renown. But if he should win the ring, it would make him lord of the world."

Siegfried thanked the bird for its counsel, and he disappeared into the cave.

Mime came out of the woods. He crept forward cautiously until he was sure the dragon was dead.

Alberich came out of his hiding place among the rocks. The two gnomes stood face to face. Each fiercely accused the other of seeking to steal the Nibelung hoard.

Long and furiously they quarreled, until Mime at last agreed to share the treasure—the Tarnhelm to him, the ring to Alberich.

"Share it with you? Give you the Tarnhelm?" Alberich laughed mockingly. "How sly you are! Never while I slept would I be safe from your cunning."

"You will leave me nothing?" asked Mime.

"Nothing at all. Not even a nailhead!" declared Alberich.

Mime trembled with fury. "Then you shall have neither ring nor Tarnhelm. I'll call Siegfried against you with his sword!"

The threat did not alarm Alberich. "Turn your head," he said. "Here he comes from the cave."

Siegfried was coming forward slowly, lost in thought.
"He has the Tarnhelm," said Alberich.

"Yes, and the ring," Mime said maliciously. "Perhaps he will give it to you!"

He slipped away into the wood.

Alberich tried to console himself. "The ring shall be surrendered to its lord at last," he said, and he disappeared into the rocky cleft.

Siegfried was meditating on his two prizes. The bird had told him to choose them from the heaped-up treasure, and so he had taken them, but they were no more than toys to him.

"They will prove that I won my fight with Fafner," he thought, "although I learned nothing of fear."

He put the Tarnhelm in his belt and the ring on his finger.

The bird began to sing again. "Hei! Siegfried now holds the helm and the ring! Let him listen sharply to Mime's treacherous words."

Siegfried gestured to show that he had understood. He stood leaning on his sword, as Mime came slinking out of the wood.

Anxious thoughts were passing through the mind of the gnome. Had the boy guessed the worth of the Tarnhelm and the ring? Had the Wanderer given him counsel? "I must be doubly cunning," he said to himself, and he moved closer to Siegfried, with fawning gestures of greeting. "Welcome, my hero. And have you learned to fear?"

Siegfried answered shortly, "I have not found the teacher."

"But you have slain the dragon. Surely he was a grim monster."

"He was fierce and dreadful, yet his death grieves me, while worse scoundrels go unpunished," said Siegfried. "The one who led me here to fight—I hate him more than the dragon."

Mime answered in his tenderest tones, but Siegfried, with his new-found wisdom, was able to hear the thoughts rather than the words of the gnome.

"So you would rob me of my sword and all I have won," said Siegfried.

"You mistake my words!" cried Mime, and he offered the drink he had prepared.

"How was it brewed?" asked Siegfried.

"Drink it and trust my skill," said Mime, but again his thoughts made themselves heard.

"You would kill me while I slept?" said Siegfried.

"When did I say that!" Mime tried to thrust the drinking horn into Siegfried's hand.

In a gesture of revulsion, Siegfried lifted his sword and struck the gnome. Mime fell dead.

Alberich had been watching from his hiding place. He laughed in gloating triumph.

Siegfried put his sword back into his belt. He picked up Mime's body, carried it to the cave, and threw it inside.

"Lie there and enjoy the treasure forever," he said. "You shall have a trusty guardian, too," and he stopped the entrance of the cave with the body of the dragon.

Suddenly he was weary. He lay down in the shade of the lime tree. In the branches overhead he saw the forest bird surrounded by its brothers and sisters, and once more he was reminded of his own lonely state. "Only one comrade was mine," he thought, "a foul and crafty gnome, who plotted against me until I was forced to slay him. Friendly bird," he called, "tell me now, could you find me a true comrade?"

The bird's song answered him. "Hei! Siegfried has slain the evil gnome. Soon he may find a glorious bride. She sleeps on a rocky height guarded by fire. He who breaks through the flames and wakes the maid Brünnhilde wins her for his own."

Siegfried sprang to his feet. "Shall I be the one to break through the flames? Can I wake the bride?"

"Only he who never has known fear shall wake Brünnhilde," sang the bird.

Siegfried shouted with joy, "I am the one who never has known fear!" He called upon the bird to show him the way to the rock where Brünnhilde lay.

The bird circled about for a little while, then flew away. Siegfried eagerly followed.

ACT 3

Through storm and darkness, Wotan, still disguised as the Wanderer, came to a wild spot at the foot of a mountain. He paused before a vaultlike hollow in the rocks and called to summon the goddess Erda, "Awake from dreams of wisdom! Awake and rise!"

Out of the hollow rose the goddess. Her hair and garments glittered as if covered with frost. She looked about her with dazed eyes.

"Who wakes me from wisdom's dream?" she asked. "Who drives my sleep away?"

"I have called you," said the Wanderer. "Boundless knowledge lives within you. I have awakened you that you may give me counsel."

She bade him go to the Norns, the three goddesses who wove the rope of fate.

The Norns had no power of their own, he answered. They could only weave as the world commanded. What he sought was someone who could change the shape of things to come.

"I bore Wotan a daughter who brought heroes to Valhalla," said Erda. "She is bold and wise. Why do you not seek counsel from her?"

"Do you mean Brünnhilde, the Valkyrie maiden?" asked the Wanderer. "She disobeyed the word of Wotan, and he placed her in a magic sleep. What counsel could come from her?"

Erda said, after a silence, "I am dazed since I awoke, and the world seems strange. My child lay bound in sleep while her mother slept? Does he who urged the doing punish the deed? Does he who upholds the truth rule by falsehood? Hold me here no longer. Let sleep again enfold my wisdom."

The Wanderer was not yet ready to let her go. Once, he said, she had planted fear in Wotan's heart by foretelling the downfall of the gods. Could she tell him now how a god might conquer his sorrow?

"You are not what you seem," said Erda. "Why did you come here to trouble my sleep?"

"Do you know what Wotan wills?" demanded the Wanderer. "Let me cry it in your ear so that you may nevermore sleep free from care!" The downfall of the gods no longer dismayed him, he said. His heritage belonged to a boy who had won the Nibelung ring—a boy free from greed and happy in his dreams of love. "This hero will wake Brünnhilde," he told the goddess. "Then the child of your wisdom will free the world. Sleep now, and in your dream look on my downfall. Go, Erda, descend to endless sleep!"

The goddess did not answer. Her eyes were already closed as she sank out of sight.

Daylight had come. The Wanderer leaned back against the rocks and looked off into the distance. He saw Siegfried approaching.

The forest bird flew into sight. When it saw the Wanderer, it stopped, fluttered its wings in alarm, and flew quickly away.

Siegfried appeared. He looked about for the bird that had been guiding him.

The Wanderer spoke. "Where does your way lead you?"

"To a mountain surrounded by fire," Siegfried told him, "where a woman lies sleeping."

"Who told you to seek the mountain?" asked the Wanderer.

"A singing wood bird," said Siegfried.

The Wanderer asked question after question, and Siegfried answered, telling of the dragon and Mime and the sword Nothung.

"Who made the mighty splinters from which you forged the sword?" asked the Wanderer.

"What do I know of that?" said Siegfried impatiently. "I only know that the splinters could not have served me if they had not been welded anew."

"That I can believe," said the Wanderer in amusement.

Siegfried was annoyed. "Why are you laughing at me and keeping me here? If you can help me find my way, speak. If you cannot, then hold your tongue."

"Good youth, have patience," said the Wanderer mildly. "If I seem old, then you should honor the aged."

"Honor the aged!" exclaimed Siegfried. "All my life an old fellow stood in my path, until I swept him away. If you stand in my way any longer, you may fare the same as Mime." He eyed the Wanderer curiously. "Why do you wear such a big hat? Why does it hang so far over your face?"

"It protects me against the wind," said the Wanderer.

"But beneath the hat you lack an eye," said Siegfried. "Surely someone struck it out when you barred his way. Be off, or you may lose the sight of the other one."

The Wanderer said, "With the eye I lack, you are now looking on the one that is left to me."

To Siegfried this was nonsense. "I'll trifle with you no longer. Help me find my way, or take yourself off."

Still speaking gently, the Wanderer said, "If you knew me, you would not scoff. It is sad to hear defiance from one so dear to me. I have long loved your race, even though it has shrunk from my fury. Do not wake my wrath today. It would ruin us both."

Siegfried ordered him to stand aside. "I know this way leads to the sleeping maid—so I was told by the wood bird that left me here alone."

"The bird fled to save its life," said the Wanderer, his voice rising in anger. "It knew that I, lord of the ravens, was here, and you shall not pass the way it pointed. By my might the sleeping maid is held enchained, and he who wakes her would make me powerless forever." He pointed with his spear toward the rocky heights. "Look, do you see the light? The clouds of fire are rolling, the flames are shooting and roaring. Go, you foolhardy boy, before they devour you!"

"Go back yourself, you babbler," said Siegfried defiantly. "I must find Brünnhilde!"

The Wanderer blocked his path. "If you have no fear of the flames, then let my spear bar your way. The sword in your hand once broke upon this shaft." He stretched out his spear. "Once again let it be broken!"

"Then I have found my father's enemy. Now I'll be revenged!" Siegfried drew his sword. With a single stroke he hewed the Wanderer's spear in two.

There was a blinding flash of lightning and a clap of thunder.

The pieces of the spear had fallen to the ground. The Wanderer stooped and picked them up.

"Advance. I cannot stop you," he said in a broken voice, and he disappeared in darkness.

Fiery clouds were descending.

90

"Glorious light! My pathway opens before me." Siegfried put his silver horn to his lips and blew an exuberant call as he plunged into the fire.

He made his way up the path. At the top of the mountain he came unharmed through the wall of flames into the light of a calm and beautiful day. He saw the precipice beyond and the woods nearby. A horse stood sleeping in the woods, and under a tree lay a sleeping figure covered with a glittering shield.

Wonderingly Siegfried drew near. He lifted the shield and disclosed what he thought to be a man in helmet and armor.

He lifted off the helmet. Long, curling hair fell about the sleeper's face.

He heard the labored breathing under the armor. With his sword he cut through the metal fastenings and took off the heavy breastplate. Brünnhilde lay before him, dressed in soft, flowing garments.

He drew back in amazement. "That is no man!" he exclaimed.

He felt himself shaken by a new emotion. A strange enchantment dazzled and blinded him.

"Where shall I call for help?" he cried. "Mother, Mother, remember me!"

Half-fainting, he sank down at Brünnhilde's side.

He must waken the maid, he thought, but how could he bear to look on the light of her eyes? He asked himself, "What is this feeling? Can it be fear?"

He moved away from the sleeping figure. The sight of her drew him back.

"Awake!" he called, but she did not stir.

He knelt and kissed her lips.

Brünnhilde awakened. He rose and stood before her. Slowly she raised herself. She greeted the sun and the light of day, and her gaze turned to Siegfried.

"Long was my sleep," she said. "What hero has awakened me?"

Siegfried was entranced by her look and her voice. "I came through the flames and lifted the helmet from your head," he said. "Siegfried's kiss has opened your eyes."

They looked at each other in ecstasy.

"Even before your birth, I cared for you and guarded you with my shield," she said.

"Your voice is wonder, even though your words are strange to me," he said.

She looked toward the woods where Grane, her sacred steed, was grazing. He had slept while she slept. Now he, too, had awakened. She saw her weapons that Wotan had placed beside her so long ago. She thought of the old life forever gone, and sadness came over her.

Siegfried tried to take her in his arms. She sprang up in fear as she realized her helplessness. No longer was she a goddess and a warrior maiden, but a mortal woman.

He spoke comfortingly until she was calm again. Still she begged him to leave her.

"If only you loved me as I love you!" said Siegfried. "Waken to live in joy and light. Be mine!"

She confessed at last that she had always loved him. She bade farewell to Valhalla and the glory of the gods. With joyous laughter, she threw herself into his arms.

THE
DUSK
OF
THE
GODS

PRELUDE

IT WAS NIGHT on Brünnhilde's mountain. In the light of the magic fire, three somberly dressed women were sitting about on the rocks. They were the three Norns, the goddesses who wove the rope of fate.

The first Norn tied one end of the golden rope to a fir tree. While she wove the strands, she sang of a time long past. Her song was of the dauntless god Wotan and how he had come to the spring of wisdom beneath the sacred ash tree. He had left one of his eyes in payment for a drink from the spring. He had wounded the tree by tearing off one of its branches. From the branch he had made the mighty shaft of his spear. Afterward the wounded tree had wasted and died, and the spring had failed.

"Now I weave no more at the world ash tree," she sang. "Now the fir tree must support the rope."

She threw the rope to the second Norn, who fastened it to a rock at the mouth of the cave nearby. The second Norn continued the song. She told how Wotan had written the sacred treaties on his spear shaft and ruled the world with his spear. A bold hero had broken the spear. Then Wotan had caused the world ash tree to be destroyed and its boughs cut to pieces.

The third Norn took her turn at weaving and singing. She sang of the gods' fortress, Valhalla, which giants had built. "There on high sits Wotan. Around the castle is the great pile of boughs cut from the world ash tree. When its wood burns, the flames shall feed on the gleaming walls, and the end of the gods shall come."

The first Norn looked at the flickering firelight on the rocks and was reminded of Loge, the fire god. "Do you know what happened to him?" she asked.

The second Norn answered. Wotan had forced him to burn as a wall of flame around Brünnhilde's rock. "Do you know what will happen now?" she asked.

The third Norn looked into the future and told what she saw. Flames would leap from the ash boughs that surrounded Valhalla.

The rope was returned to the first Norn. As she tried to weave its strands, she recalled Alberich, the gnome, who had robbed the Rhinemaidens of their gold. "What was his fate?" she asked.

The second Norn took the rope and fastened it to a stone. She cried out that the curse of the Nibelung ring was gnawing at the strands.

The third Norn caught the rope. It broke in her hands.

"Here ends our wisdom!" cried the Norns. "The world shall hear us no more. Away to Mother—away!"

They disappeared, descending toward the dwelling place of Erda, the earth goddess.

The sun had risen, and against the morning sky the glow of the fire could no longer be seen.

Siegfried and Brünnhilde came out of the cave. Brünnhilde was leading her horse, Grane. Siegfried was fully armed, and he carried Brünnhilde's shield. He was the bold hero of whom the Norns had sung. He had won the Tarnhelm and the Rhinegold from the giant, Fafner. With his sword, Nothung, he had broken Wotan's spear, and he had braved the fire to waken Brünnhilde from her enchanted sleep.

Once, as Wotan's favorite daughter, Brünnhilde had led the wild, free life of a Valkyrie. Now she had become a mortal woman, and Siegfried was her beloved master.

"What the gods taught me I have given to you," she said. "I am rich in love, but poor in power."

Siegfried was ready to return to the world, to new and great exploits. She asked him to remember her and the vows that bound them together.

Siegfried took the ring—the Rhinegold—from his finger. "The virtue of my deeds lies in this," he said. "Guard it well in token of my love."

Brünnhilde put the ring on her own finger. "Never shall it be taken from my hand." In exchange for the ring, she gave him her horse. "Once he flew with me through the heavens," she said. "Now, like myself, he has lost his magic powers, yet wherever you lead Grane will follow without fear."

They bade each other farewell. She watched him lead Grane out of sight. She stood alone, listening to the sound of Siegfried's horn in the distance.

ACT 1

In a great hall overlooking the River Rhine sat Gunther, king of the Gibichungs. His sister, Gutrune, sat beside him. Across the table from them was their swarthy and sinister-looking half-brother, Hagen.

Gunther and Gutrune were the children of Gibich, the former king. Hagen was fathered by Alberich, the Nibelung who had once robbed the Rhinemaidens of the Rhinegold.

Gunther was asking Hagen, "Tell me truly, is my fame on the Rhine worthy of my father's name?"

"I am envious of your glory," answered Hagen.

"And I envy you," said Gunther. "I inherited the first-born's right, but wisdom was left to you." Again he asked of his renown in the land.

"Your fame is flawed," admitted Hagen, "for I know of rare treasures not yet won by the Gibichungs. You are yet without a wife, and you, Gutrune, have no husband."

The king and his sister meditated silently for a while. Gunther asked, "Whom should I wed that new fame may come to us?"

Hagen told him, "A wife waits for you, the noblest in the world. Her home is on a mountain rock surrounded by fire, and only he who breaks through the flames may win her."

"Am I fit for the task?" asked Gunther.

Hagen answered that it was reserved for a mightier man—the hero Siegfried. "It would be well," he added, "if Gutrune wedded him."

Gutrune asked shyly how the hero had won his fame.

Siegfried had slain the dragon and won for himself the treasure of the Nibelung, said Hagen.

"He alone may win Brünnhilde?" asked Gunther.

"None other may pass through the fire," said Hagen.

Gunther rose and began to stride up and down. "Why do you waken this discord and doubt?" he asked. "Why do you rouse my desire for delights I may not win?"

"If Siegfried should win the bride," said Hagen, "would she not then be yours?"

"How could I force him to win the bride for me?" demanded Gunther.

Hagen slyly suggested that Gutrune might cast a spell over Siegfried.

Wounded and angry, Gutrune accused Hagen of evil and mockery. "What spell have I? If he is the greatest of heroes, the most beautiful women on earth must long since have won his love!"

Hagen leaned toward her and said in a confidential tone, "Do you recall the drink in the chest yonder? Trust in me who brought it home. It will bind any man to you. Tell me now—how do you like my plan?"

Gunther praised him warmly, and Gutrune wished that Siegfried might come.

"How can he be found?" asked Gunther.

As he spoke, the sound of a horn was heard.

Hagen looked out through the back of the hall to the River Rhine and saw a boat approaching. A man and a horse were in the boat. The man blew a hunting horn while he drove the boat along with an easy, indolent hand. "There can be only one so mighty," said Hagen. "It is Siegfried and none other." Through cupped hands he hailed the man: "Hoi-ho! Whom do you seek?"

Siegfried called back that he sought Gibich's son.

"His hall awaits you here," said Hagen.

Siegfried landed and led his horse ashore. Graciously Gunther introduced himself as Gibich's son.

"Your fame has spread far along the Rhine," Siegfried greeted him. "Fight with me now, or be my friend."

"Come in peace," said Gunther.

Hagen led Siegfried's horse away. At the same time he made a sign to Gutrune, and she slipped away into her room.

Gunther offered his hospitality to the hero.

Siegfried answered that he could offer no hospitality in return. "I have neither land nor folk nor house. I am

98

heir only to my life and limbs, and I have the sword I made."

Hagen had returned. "There is a rumor," he said, "that you are also lord of the Nibelung's hoard."

The hoard meant so little to Siegfried that he had forgotten it. "I left it lying in the cave," he said, "where a dragon watched over it."

"And you took nothing from it?" asked Hagen.

Siegfried pointed to the steel network which he wore in his belt. He had taken it from the heap of treasure, he said, although he did not know of what use it was.

Hagen recognized it as the Tarnhelm, the Nibelung's cunningest work. "When it is set on your head, you may change to any shape at will. Or if you wish to go to far-off lands, the Tarnhelm will take you there in an instant. Did you take nothing else from the hoard?"

"A ring," said Siegfried. "It is worn by a woman."

"Brünnhilde!" Hagen said to himself.

He summoned Gutrune. She came out of her room carrying a drinking horn, which she handed to Siegfried.

He bowed pleasantly, took the horn, and drank. Gutrune looked down in embarrassment.

Almost at once Siegfried began to feel the effects of the potion in the drink. He gazed ardently into Gutrune's face. He seized her hand and asked if he might offer himself to her.

Shamed now, and humble, she lowered her head and left the hall.

Siegfried's eyes followed her. He asked Gunther, "Have you a wife?"

"I am not wed yet," said Gunther. "I have set my heart on one I can never win."

"How could you fail," asked Siegfried, "with me as a friend?"

"Her home is on a rock surrounded by fire," said Gunther.

Siegfried repeated the words as if he were making an intense effort to recall something.

"And who breaks through the fire is Brünnhilde's fitting mate," Gunther said.

Siegfried heard Brünnhilde's name with no sign of recollection. "I fear no fire. I will win this bride for you if you will give me Gutrune as my wife."

"Gladly I give you Gutrune," said Gunther.

"Then Brünnhilde shall be yours," promised Siegfried.

"How will you persuade her?" asked Gunther.

"Through the magic of the Tarnhelm I shall change my shape for yours," said Siegfried.

Hagen filled a drinking horn with wine and held it out to them. With their swords, Siegfried and Gunther cut their arms and held them for a few moments over the horn. Then, as they drank the wine, they swore an oath of blood brotherhood.

After they had drunk, Hagen struck the horn in two with his sword.

Siegfried asked him why he had taken no part in the ceremony.

"My blood would be poison to your drink," said Hagen. "It is not pure and free like yours."

Siegfried took up his shield and motioned to Gunther.

Gunther placed the care of the homestead in Hagen's hands. Then he followed Siegfried to the boat.

Gutrune came out into the hall. "Where are they going so quickly?" she asked.

"They are sailing to find Brünnhilde," said Hagen. "See how Siegfried makes haste, so that he may win you!"

"Siegfried, mine!" sighed Gutrune longingly, and she went back into her room.

Hagen sat alone in the hall. He saw the boat sail.

"Here I sit on guard," he said. "The Gibich's son sails forth to his wooing, and a hero steers the boat. The hero will bring his rightful bride to the Rhine, and with her—the ring." He spoke softly, his voice sinister and cold. "You sons of freedom, sail merrily on. To you I may seem mean and low, but you both shall serve the Nibelung's son!"

On the mountaintop, Brünnhilde sat gazing at the ring on her finger—the ring Siegfried had given her. The sound of a storm aroused her. She looked up to see a thundercloud coming near. Borne on the cloud were a horse and rider.

At the time of her exile, Wotan had forbidden her Valkyrie sisters to come near her, and Brünnhilde was astonished to recognize the rider as her sister Waltraute.

"Have you come to me?" she called. "Leave your horse there."

She ran into the woods to greet her sister. The two returned together. Brünnhilde hoped Wotan had forgiven her. It was true that she had defied him by defending

THE DUSK OF THE GODS

Siegfried's father, yet she was sure she had acted according to Wotan's secret wishes. She was sure, too, that Wotan was no longer angry. Although he had left her here in an enchanted sleep, he had surrounded her with a wall of fire that barred all but the bravest of heroes. "So my punishment brought me the greatest of blessings," she told her sister. "The noblest hero has won me for his wife. I live in laughter and light, blessed by his love. Have you come here to share in my joy?"

"Share the madness that has seized your brain?" returned Waltraute impatiently. "Calm your frenzy and listen to me." She told Brünnhilde that Wotan no longer sent his Valkyrie daughters to bring the slain heroes to Valhalla. After turning from Brünnhilde, he had roamed the world disguised as the Wanderer, and one day he had come home carrying his splintered spear shaft, which a hero had broken. He had sent Valhalla's heroes to hew the world ash tree to pieces, and now the pieces were stacked about the castle walls. He had sent his two ravens forth in the hope that they would bring back good tidings.

"I pressed myself, weeping, upon his breast," she said, "and his eyes grew soft as he remembered you. He spoke these words: 'If ever the Rhinemaidens win the ring from Brünnhilde's hand, the gods and the world will be released from the curse.' Then I stole away and secretly rode to you."

She knelt and begged her sister to do what she could to end the grief of the gods.

At first Brünnhilde did not understand what Waltraute was asking, and when she did understand she was outraged. "Give the Rhinemaidens the ring? The pledge of Siegfried's love? Have you lost your senses!"

Waltraute's voice rose wildly. "Cast the ring away! Throw the accursed thing into the flood!"

"How can you understand what it is to me, loveless maid?" said Brünnhilde. "Go to the holy council of the gods and tell them they shall never take my love from me, even though Valhalla falls to ruins!"

"Woe is me!" cried Waltraute. "Woe to you, sister, and the gods of Valhalla!" And she rushed away.

It was evening. The light of the fire had begun to shine more brightly from below.

As Brünnhilde stood looking out on the landscape, she heard the sound of a horn.

Her first thought was that Siegfried had returned. Joyfully she ran to meet him.

Fire shot up over the rocks. Out of the flames stepped Siegfried.

Brünnhilde shrank back. The Tarnhelm covered the upper half of his face, leaving only his eyes visible. He had come to her in the form of Gunther.

In a strange, rough voice, he spoke. "Brünnhilde! A wooer comes who does not fear the fire. I seek you for my wife."

"Who is this man?" asked Brünnhilde in terror.

"A hero who shall tame you," answered Siegfried. "I am a Gibichung, and Gunther is the name of the one you shall follow now."

Brünnhilde cried out in dismay, thinking that Wotan had sent this shame and sorrow upon her.

"The night draws on," said Siegfried. "Within your cave you must be wedded to me."

She stretched out her hand. "Go back. This ring is my guard!"

"With this ring you shall wed Gunther," he said. He seized her. They struggled furiously, and he tore the ring from her finger.

"Now you are mine," he said triumphantly. "Brünnhilde—Gunther's bride!"

He drove her into the cave. He drew his sword and called on it to bear witness that he had kept his promise to Gunther. "Let your blade safeguard his bride," he said, and he followed Brünnhilde into the cave.

ACT 2

In the hour before dawn, Hagen sat before the hall of the Gibichungs. He was sleeping, with his arm around his spear and his head against a wooden pillar. Before him crouched Alberich, the gnome, leaning his arms on Hagen's knees.

"Do you sleep, my son?" asked Alberich softly.

Hagen answered, without moving, "I hear you well. What have you to tell my slumber?"

"Never forget the might that is yours," said Alberich. "Hate the happy. Be cunning, strong, and bold. Even now our enemies are dismayed by our hate. Wotan, who robbed me of my ring, has himself been vanquished. I fear him no more."

105

Hagen asked in his sleep, "Who shall inherit the power of the gods?"

"I—and you," said Alberich. "The world will be ours." Between them, he said, they must bring about Siegfried's undoing. It was true that Alberich had placed a curse on the ring, but the curse had no effect on Siegfried because the hero knew nothing of the Rhinegold's true worth. If he should give the ring back to the Rhinemaidens, the gold would be forever lost to the Nibelungs.

"Therefore strive for the ring," he said. "Swear to me, Hagen, my son."

Hagen answered, "I will have the ring. Rest in peace."

"Be true, Hagen, my son. Be true." Alberich's voice had grown fainter. His form faded until it disappeared.

The red glow of dawn had spread over the river. Siegfried came into sight on the shore. He still wore the Tarnhelm, but he had changed to his own shape. On his way toward the hall, he took the metal work from his head and hung it on his belt.

He had just come from Brünnhilde's rock, he told Hagen. Through the magic of the Tarnhelm he had flown home as quickly as he could draw a breath. Two others were coming more slowly in the boat.

He asked that Gutrune be called, so that both she and Hagen could hear of his triumph.

Gutrune came out of the hall.

"Today I have won you for my wife!" said Siegfried. He told how he had changed his shape to that of Gunther and passed unharmed through the flames to Brünnhilde's rock. In the morning Brünnhilde had followed him down

106

through the dying fire. When they were near the river he had managed to change places with Gunther. Now, he said, a driving wind was bringing the pair to the Gibichungs' hall.

"Siegfried—mightiest man!" said Gutrune adoringly. "What fear I feel of you!" She began to plan for Brünnhilde's coming and for the wedding to follow. "You, Hagen, call the men together, while I call the maidens to the feast."

She and Siegfried went into the hall together. Hagen stationed himself on a rocky height back of the hall and blew several loud blasts on a horn.

Other horn calls answered, and soon the Gibichung vassals began to gather on the shore. They believed they had been called to defend the hall, and they asked what enemy was near.

Hagen announced that they were here to welcome their lord, who was bringing a wife to Gibichung hall. He directed them to make sacrifices to the gods. Afterward they were to join in feasting and drinking.

The men laughed at the spectacle of grim-faced Hagen in the role of wedding herald.

Grave and unbending as ever, Hagen ordered them to leave off laughing and receive Gunther's bride. "Love your lady well and give her your aid, and if she should be wronged, be swift with your vengeance!"

Men were watching from the heights, and they began to call out, "Hail!" as the boat carrying Gunther and Brünnhilde came near. Others waded into the water and drew the boat to land.

Gunther helped Brünnhilde ashore. The vassals struck their weapons noisily together and shouted a welcome.

Brünnhilde's face was pale, her eyes cast down. Proudly Gunther presented her.

Siegfried and Gutrune came out of the hall, followed by a group of women.

"I greet you, my hero, and you, loving sister," said Gunther. "Two happy couples shall find blessing in wedlock. Brünnhilde and Gunther—Gutrune and Siegfried."

Brünnhilde looked at Siegfried in stunned amazement.

"Siegfried—here?" she faltered. "Gutrune?"

"Gunther's gentle sister," said Siegfried, "won by me, as you are won by him."

"I? Gunther?" Brünnhilde cried with fearful vehemence. "You lie!"

She staggered and would have fallen if Siegfried had not caught her.

She looked into his face. "Siegfried—does not know me?" she said faintly.

Gunther came to her side, and Siegfried pointed to him. "Here stands your husband."

She saw the ring on Siegfried's outstretched hand. She gave a terrible cry. "The ring—? He—? Siegfried—?"

Hagen came forward. "Now listen well to the woman's tale," he said.

Brünnhilde was struggling to control her emotions. She said to Siegfried, "On your hand I saw a ring. It was taken from me, not by you, but by this man!" She pointed to Gunther. "How did the ring come from his hand to yours?"

108

"The ring did not come from him," said Siegfried.

Brünnhilde turned on Gunther. "This ring with which I wedded you—take it back again!"

He answered in perplexity that he had given Siegfried no ring.

"Then where are you hiding the ring you stole from my hand?" she asked.

Gunther stood silent and confused.

"Ha! Siegfried's the man who robbed me of the ring," cried Brünnhilde in a passion. "Siegfried, the traitor and thief!"

Siegfried denied that he had stolen the ring. He had won it, he said, when he killed the mighty dragon.

Hagen intervened. "Brünnhilde, do you know the ring well? If it is the one that Gunther took from you, then it is his, and Siegfried won it by trickery."

In terrible anguish, Brünnhilde called on the gods to teach her such vengeance as had never been known before. "That man standing there—I am his wife!"

The vassals and women were amazed. "Siegfried?" they said to one another. "Gutrune's husband?"

Siegfried, still under the spell of Hagen's magic potion, denied that he was Brünnhilde's husband or that he had ever broken faith with Gunther.

But the Gibichungs had begun to eye Siegfried doubtfully and to mutter among themselves. Both Gunther and Gutrune called on him to speak and prove Brünnhilde's charges false.

Siegfried offered to swear an oath.

Hagen held out his spear. Siegfried laid two fingers of

his right hand on the spear point. "Shining steel," he said, "deal death to me if I have wronged the woman or if I am false to my friend."

Brünnhilde thrust herself into the group of men surrounding Siegfried. She seized the spear point in her own hand. "Shining steel," she cried, "I pray that he may die by your point, for he has sworn to falsehood, and all his vows are broken!"

Siegfried said sternly to Gunther, "Look to the woman. Let her rest awhile, until her madness has spent itself." He said in a lower voice, "I suspect the Tarnhelm was only half a disguise. But woman's anger is quickly gone. Surely she will yet give thanks that I have won her for you." He urged the vassals to join the women in merry-

making. "Show your gladness—be as happy as I!" and he threw his arm about Gutrune and swept her away into the hall. The men and women trooped after him, until only Brünnhilde, Gunther, and Hagen were left behind.

Gunther was shamed and troubled. He seated himself apart from the others and covered his face with his hands. Brünnhilde gazed fixedly after Siegfried and Gutrune for a while. Then her head drooped. "What evil lies hidden here?" she wondered. "How can I solve the riddle? All my wisdom I gave to him. I am held in his bondage. Who will lend me the sword with which I might cut the bonds!"

Hagen moved close to her. "Give me your trust," he said. "I will avenge your wrong."

She smiled bitterly. A single glance from Siegfried, she said, would cast dismay over Hagen's daring.

"Well I know Siegfried's conquering might," he said. "But whisper to me some cunning spell to make him weak in my hands."

She had no arts and spells left for him, she answered. She had given them all to Siegfried, and now they kept him safe from harm.

"Then no blade can harm him?" asked Hagen.

He could be wounded only in the back, she said. She had given him no spell to protect him there because there was no need. In battle he never turned his back to an enemy.

"There my spear will strike!" Hagen turned to Gunther. "Here stands your brave wife. Why do you bow your head in grief?"

"Oh, shame! Oh, sorrow!" cried Gunther. "Woe is me, most distressed of men!"

"Cowardly man—treacherous friend," said Brünnhilde contemptuously, "hiding behind the hero so that he might win you the reward of victory! Your race sank low when you were born!"

"I am the deceived and the deceiver—the betrayed and the betrayer." Gunther appealed to Hagen. "Help, help for my honor!"

Hagen answered, "Nothing helps but Siegfried's death."

Gunther shrank from the thought. "We swore blood brotherhood."

"He betrayed both you and me," said Brünnhilde.

Hagen said close to Gunther's ear, "His fall will bring you gain. All the world will be at your command if you can win from him the ring that only death can make him surrender."

"Brünnhilde's ring?" asked Gunther.

"The Nibelung ring," said Hagen.

Gunther thought of Gutrune. "How could we stand before her with Siegfried's blood on our hands?"

At the mention of Gutrune's name, Brünnhilde started up in rage. "She holds the spell that took my love from me. May ill fate be hers!"

"We must keep the deed hidden from her," said Hagen. "Tomorrow we go hunting. The bold hero may be brought home struck by a boar!"

Gunther agreed at last that Siegfried must fall.

"So shall it be," said he and Brünnhilde, and Hagen echoed the words.

The bridal procession came out of the hall. Vassals were carrying Siegfried on a shield. Others bore Gutrune on a chair. Boys and girls ran before them scattering flowers in their path. Men and women climbed the heights back of the hall, preparing to make sacrifices on the altars that were there.

Siegfried and some of the vassals sounded the wedding call on their horns. Gutrune smilingly beckoned Brünnhilde to come to her side.

Brünnhilde would have stood aloof if Hagen had not intervened. He pushed her toward Gunther, who grasped her hand and drew her into the procession. The bridal party passed, until only Hagen was left behind.

ACT 3

Out of the River Rhine rose the three Rhinemaidens, Woglinde, Wellgunde, and Flosshilde. As they swam about, they lamented the loss of their shining treasure, the Rhinegold, which Alberich had stolen from them long ago.

A hunting horn sounded. They recognized it as the horn of the hero who might restore their lost gold, and they dived below to wait for him.

Siegfried came in sight on a cliff above the river. He had left the rest of the hunters and lost his way. Now the bear he had been following was lost, as well.

The Rhinemaidens swam to the surface and called him by name.

113

Good-humoredly he asked them if they had lured away the shaggy fellow he had been hunting.

"What will you give us if we give back your game?" asked Woglinde.

"Today I am empty-handed," he said.

"A golden ring gleams on your finger," said Wellgunde, and the three maidens spoke in chorus, "Give us that!"

"I won the ring from a dragon," said Siegfried. "Should I give it in exchange for a worthless bearskin?"

"Are you so mean?" said Woglinde.

"So miserly?" said Wellgunde.

"You should always be generous with maids," said Flosshilde.

"If I waste my goods on you," he answered, "my wife will scold me."

Was the hero afraid of his wife? they asked.

They could joke as much as they pleased, he said, but their mockery would never win the ring.

This man was so handsome and strong, the maidens said to one another; what a pity he was such a miser. Laughing, they dived out of sight.

In spite of himself, he was stung by their gibes. He came down the cliff to the river bank. "Here!" he called. "I grant you the ring!"

The Rhinemaidens rose again to the surface, and now their faces were grave. "Keep the ring until you know the ill fortune it holds," they said. "Then you will be glad to let us free you from the curse."

Quietly Siegfried replaced the ring on his finger. "Tell me what you know," he said.

They warned him of evil that awaited him. The ring was wrought of the Rhine's pure gold, and he who had shaped and lost it placed a curse on it. "As you slew the dragon," they said, "so shall you be slain, and here today, unless you yield the ring to rest in the river forever."

"Say no more," said Siegfried. "If your craft could not deceive me, your threats will frighten me even less."

The maidens begged him to heed their counsel. The Norns had woven the curse into the rope of fate, they said, but he still might escape it.

"My sword once shattered a spear," he told them. "If a curse has been spun into the rope of fate, my sword shall cut it asunder." He went on to tell them he had felt no fear when the dragon warned him of the curse. The Rhinegold had given him the world's wealth, yet for the grace of love he would freely have given it to the maidens just now. But the ring could not be taken from him by a threat. "My life and limbs mean no more to me than this," he said, and he picked up a clod of earth and tossed it carelessly behind him.

"Come, sisters, let us fly from this man," said the Rhinemaidens. "He fancies himself brave and wise, but he walks in bonds and blindness. The glorious gift he once had is lost to him, and he holds to the ring which will deal him death. This day a proud woman will inherit your wealth, and she will hear our prayer." They turned from him and swam away.

Siegfried reflected that women were always the same, on land or water. If a man did not yield to their smiles, they threatened him. If he scorned their threats, they stung him with scolding tongues. "And yet," he mused, "if I were not true to Gutrune, I would have captured one of those pretty maidens for my own."

The rest of the hunting party had come in search of him. The men were shouting and blowing their horns.

Siegfried shouted and blew his horn in reply.

Hagen and Gunther came into sight on the cliff.

"Come down," called Siegfried. "It is fresh and cool here."

Hagen and Gunther, followed by the vassals, came down to the shore.

"Here we will rest and prepare the meal," said Hagen, and the hunters stacked their game in a heap and brought out wineskins and drinking horns.

Siegfried admitted that he had been unlucky in the chase. "I hunted for wood game, but I found only water-fowl. If I had reckoned rightly, I might have brought you three water birds who sang that I should be slain."

Gunther looked guiltily at Hagen.

"It would be grievous if a lurking beast should slay the luckless hunter," said Hagen.

Siegfried sat down. Hagen handed him a drinking horn of wine. "I have heard, Siegfried," he said, "that when birds are singing you can understand their speech. Can that be true?"

"Long ago I put their words out of my mind," said Siegfried.

He drank, then offered the horn to Gunther.

"The wine is poor and pale," said Gunther, shuddering as he looked into the horn. "Your blood alone is there!"

"Then let our blood be mingled." Siegfried poured wine from Gunther's horn into his own until it overflowed. "Now here's an offering to Mother Earth."

"You overjoyous man!" sighed Gunther.

Siegfried asked Hagen, "Has Brünnhilde made him sad?"

Hagen answered, "Her voice is not so clear to him as the song of birds is to you."

"Since women have sung their songs to me, I have forgotten the songs of birds." Siegfried turned to Gunther. "Hei, gloomy man! If it will amuse you, I'll tell you some wonderful tales of my boyhood."

The others lay down about Siegfried, and he began. He told of his early years with Mime, the gnome, who brought him up fearless and strong so that he might slay Fafner, the dragon. He told how he had forged the broken blade of Nothung, his father's sword, and with it killed the dragon. "The blood of the creature burned my fingers, and I raised them to my mouth," he said, "and straightway I understood the speech of the birds."

He told of the forest bird that had directed him to take from the dragon's hoard only the Tarnhelm and the ring, and how the bird had warned him against Mime.

"The warning was good?" asked Hagen.

"Nothung paid him his wage," answered Siegfried.

Hagen had had another drinking horn filled, and he squeezed the juice of an herb into it. "Drink, hero," he said. "This will awaken your remembrance so that none of the past may escape you."

Siegfried drained the horn. At once the memory of his

first meeting with Brünnhilde was restored. He began to tell of the glorious bride guarded by fire and how he had braved the flames and wakened the maiden with a kiss.

Gunther spoke in amazement. "What is he saying!"

Two ravens flew up, circled over Siegfried, and flew away toward the river.

"Can you read me the speech of those birds?" asked Hagen.

Siegfried stood up and, with his back to Hagen, looked after the birds. Hagen thrust his spear into Siegfried's back.

Siegfried swung his shield high with both hands and made a motion to crush Hagen beneath it, but his strength failed. The shield fell, and he fell upon it.

"What deed is this?" cried Gunther and the vassals.

"Falsehood's payment!" answered Hagen. He left the others and walked away through the gathering dusk.

Gunther was stricken with grief. He bent over Siegfried, and two of the vassals gently raised the dying man.

For a little while Siegfried believed that Brünnhilde was there. He spoke to her tenderly. Then he sank back and died.

At a mute command from Gunther, several vassals lifted Siegfried's body on his shield and carried it away. The others followed in a solemn procession, as the moon broke through the clouds and mists rose slowly from the Rhine.

In the hall of the Gibichungs, Gutrune waited for Siegfried to come from the hunt. Evil dreams had disturbed

her sleep. Siegfried's horse had neighed wildly. She had heard Brünnhilde's strange laughter, and she had seen a woman go down to the shore.

She listened at Brünnhilde's door. She called, then looked into the room. Brünnhilde was gone.

From far away came the sound of a hunting horn, but it was not Siegfried's horn.

She heard Hagen shouting, "Hoi ho, hoi ho! Awake, awake!"

Hagen entered the hall. "Up, Gutrune, and greet your Siegfried," he said. "The hero is coming home."

"I did not hear his horn," she said fearfully.

"The pale hero will blow it no more," said Hagen.

Men and women bearing lights and firebrands came into the hall, accompanying the procession that had come home with Siegfried's body.

Gutrune watched in growing horror. Men put the body down in the middle of the hall.

"A wild boar has slain him," said Hagen.

Gutrune shrieked and fell upon Siegfried's body.

Gunther had come into the hall. He bent over his sister and tried to comfort her.

Gutrune shrank from him. "You have slain my husband!"

"Do not blame me. Blame Hagen instead," said Gunther. "He has slain the hero."

Hagen threw off his pretense. "Yes, I did slay him. He swore a false oath on my spear. I have won the right of heritage, and I claim the ring."

"The ring is mine!" said Gunther.

120

Hagen rushed upon him with drawn sword. They fought furiously. Before the vassals could separate them, Hagen had struck Gunther dead.

"Now the ring!" cried Hagen. He grasped at the ring on Siegfried's finger.

Siegfried's hand rose threateningly. Hagen drew back, and a wave of terror swept over the assembled group.

Brünnhilde came slowly forward from the rear of the hall.

Out of the wisdom regained through suffering, she spoke with solemn dignity. "The wife whom you have all betrayed now comes for vengeance. Your cries are like the weeping of children complaining because milk has been spilled. I have heard no lament fit for the death of the greatest hero."

Gutrune raised herself from the floor and wildly accused Brünnhilde, "You have brought this curse upon us. It was you who roused the men against him!"

"Peace, poor soul," said Brünnhilde. "You were never Siegfried's wife. All his vows he had sworn to me before he ever looked on your face."

Gutrune looked at Hagen in sudden understanding. "It was the hateful potion you gave that stole her husband away. Oh, sorrow! All is clear to me now."

She sank down beside Siegfried's body. Hagen stood defiantly leaning on his spear and shield.

Brünnhilde had come to the center of the hall, and for a while she gazed raptly on Siegfried's face. Then she turned toward the others with a look of exaltation.

"Bring mighty logs and pile them high by the river

shore," she said. "Kindle a bright, fierce fire, and let the body of the noblest hero be consumed in its flames. Bring me his horse, so that with me he may follow his master."

The vassals raised a huge funeral pyre near the shore of the river. The women covered the logs with draperies and flowers.

Brünnhilde's face had taken on an expression of soft brightness. Now she understood that for all his broken promises, Siegfried had always been true. It was his ill fate that the doom of the gods had fallen upon him.

She looked upward, directing her words to Wotan. "See the guilt that is yours."

At a sign from her, some of the men placed Siegfried's body on the pyre. She took the ring from his finger.

"Terrible ring!" she said. "I grasp it and throw it away. Listen, you sisters who live in the water—what you desire I leave to you. From my ashes take your treasure. Let the fire cleanse it of its curse. You in the flood, keep the gold forever shining and pure."

She had put the ring on her finger. She took a firebrand from one of the men, and she called out so that Wotan's ravens could hear, "Fly home and tell your lord what you have learned here on the Rhine. Fly first to Brünnhilde's rock where Loge burns. Bid him go straightway to Valhalla, for the dusk of the gods draws near. So I hurl the brand on Valhalla's walls."

She flung the firebrand on the logs. The pyre burst into flame.

Two ravens flew up from the rocks by the shore and were quickly out of sight.

Brünnhilde saw the horse Grane, which had just been led in. She took off his bridle and spoke to him affectionately. "Do you know where I lead you and to whom? We go to greet our lord."

She mounted the horse and urged him forward. He leaped with her into the flaming pyre.

The fire blazed up, enveloping the space in front of the hall and seizing on the building itself. The men and women crowded together in terror.

Suddenly the flames subsided until only a cloud of smoke remained. At the same time the Rhine swelled in a flood that swept over the fire. On the waves rode the three Rhinemaidens.

Hagen threw aside his sword and shield and went plunging toward them like a madman.

"The ring is mine!" he cried.

Woglinde and Wellgunde wound their arms about him and dragged him down with them into the water. Flosshilde had recovered the ring from the ashes. She swam in front of the others, holding the Rhinegold high.

A glow broke through the smoke cloud and lighted the Rhine that had sunk back into its bed. In its calm waters the Rhinemaidens were swimming in circles, joyously playing with the ring.

The glow deepened, and in the sky appeared the interior of Valhalla, with the gods and heroes assembled, awaiting their doom. The fire blazed up, rising higher until the dwelling of the gods was enveloped in flames.

CASTS OF CHARACTERS

THE RHINEGOLD

Woglinde	Soprano
Wellgunde	Soprano
Flosshilde	Mezzo-soprano
Alberich	Bass-baritone
Fricka	Mezzo-soprano
Wotan	Bass-baritone
Freia	Soprano
Fasolt	Bass
Fafner	Bass
Froh	Tenor
Donner	Baritone
Loge	Tenor
Mime	Tenor
Erda	Mezzo-soprano

THE VALKYRIE

Siegmund	Tenor
Sieglinde	Soprano
Hunding	Bass
Wotan	Bass-baritone
Brünnhilde	Soprano
Fricka	Mezzo-soprano
The Valkyries	Sopranos and Contraltos

SIEGFRIED

Siegfried	Tenor
Mime	Tenor
The Wanderer	Bass-baritone
Alberich	Bass-baritone
Fafner	Bass
Erda	Mezzo-soprano
The Forest Bird	Soprano
Brünnhilde	Soprano

THE DUSK OF THE GODS

First Norn	Contralto
Second Norn	Mezzo-soprano

Third Norn	Soprano
Siegfried	Tenor
Brünnhilde	Soprano
Gunther	Bass-baritone
Gutrune	Soprano
Hagen	Bass
Alberich	Bass-baritone
Waltraute	Mezzo-soprano
Woglinde	Soprano
Wellgunde	Soprano
Flosshilde	Mezzo-soprano

126

THEMES
FROM
THE
OPERAS

The Rhinegold

The River Rhine theme:

Song of the Rhinemaidens:

The Rhinegold theme: Theme of the Ring:

Theme of Valhalla:

The Treaty theme:

Freia's plea for help:

Approach of the giants:

Freia's theme:

Loge's fire-music: **Music of the anvils:**

Tarnhelm theme:

Mime's theme:

Dragon theme:

Alberich's curse:

Erda's theme: **Sword theme:**

Rhinemaidens' lament:

The Valkyrie

Storm music:

Sieglinde's tenderness: **Love theme:**

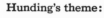

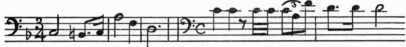

Theme of Siegmund's sorrow: **Hunding's theme:**

Theme of the Wälsungs:

Cry of victory: **Siegmund's love song:**

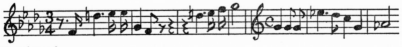

Theme of Sieglinde's love: **Theme of Siegmund's love:**

**Naming of
the sword:**   **Ride of the Valkyries:**

Valkyries' battle cry: **Theme of Fricka's anger:**

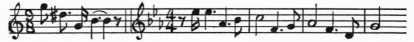

Theme of Wotan's grief: **Theme of death:**

Theme of Siegfried, the hero:

Theme of love's redemption: **Wälsungs' love theme:**

Theme of Brünnhilde's exile: **Brünnhilde's slumber music:**

Wotan's farewell to Brünnhilde:

Magic Fire music:

Siegfried

Theme of the treasure hoard:

Siegfried's horn-call:

Theme of Siegfried's youth and vigor:

Siegfried's song of freedom:

Wanderer's theme:

Theme of the gods:

Siegfried's forging song:

Forest murmurs:

Song of the forest bird:

Theme of Wotan's heritage:

Brünnhilde's awakening:

131

Themes from the love duet of Brünnhilde and Siegfried:

The Dusk of the Gods

Theme of the Norns:

Theme of the gods' downfall:

Siegfried, the hero:

Brünnhilde, the woman: Love theme:

Theme of Hagen:

Theme of the Gibichungs:

**Theme of the friendship
of Siegfried and Gunther:**   **Theme of Gutrune:**

The magic potion: **Oath of brotherhood:**

Theme of the plot against Siegfried's life:

Song of the Rhinemaidens:

The Rhinemaidens' warning:

Siegfried's funeral march:

Theme of love's redemption:

133

INDEX

ABOUT THE AUTHOR

Clyde Robert Bulla is a writer and a musician. He wrote his first
stories and composed his first songs when he attended a one-room
school near King City, Missouri. Since that time Mr. Bulla has written
innumerable books for boys and girls, all of them highly successful with
both children and adults.

When he is not writing stories, Mr. Bulla most enjoys composing and
listening to music, particularly opera. He has always felt that there
was a need for books that tell the stories of the operas clearly and
dramatically. In *Stories of Favorite Operas* and *The Ring and
the Fire* Mr. Bulla fills this need admirably.

ABOUT THE ARTISTS

Clare Romano Ross and John Ross were trained at Cooper Union
School of Art and studied at the Ecole des Beaux Arts, Fontainebleau,
France, and at the Istituto Statale, Florence, Italy. The Rosses were
awarded Tiffany Fellowships for printmaking and lived in Italy for a
year under a Fulbright grant for woodcuts. They are represented in
museums throughout the United States and their work is in the permanent
collection of the Metropolitan Museum of Art.

Mr. and Mrs. Ross live and work in New Jersey, a short distance from
New York City where they teach. Mr. Ross is President of the Society
of American Graphic Artists.